The Ignored Pandemic:

Real Stories of Lyme Disease

Kenzie Vath

© 2023 Kindle Direct Publishing

Kenzie Vath
The Ignored Pandemic: Real Stories of Lyme Disease

Disclaimer

The Ignored Pandemic: Real Stories of Lyme Disease is intended to share general information regarding Lyme Disease as well as a collection of interviews from Lyme warriors globally. The Ignored Pandemic does not claim to provide medical advice or diagnostic direction. Readers should not consider the book a substitution for professional medical advice, diagnostics, or treatment for Lyme Disease or other tick-borne diseases.

Published by: Kindle Direct Publishing
Text Design by: Kenzie Vath
Cover Design by: Kenzie Vath

Paperback ISBN: 978-1-961472-50-1
Hardcover ISBN: 978- 1-961472-51-8

Distributed by:
Amazon
410 Terry Ave N,
Seattle, WA, 98109

Do not give up the Fight
You are a Lyme Warrior

Dedication

A simple thank you does not nearly express my gratitude to all the Lyme Warriors who have shared their stories vulnerably in the pages to come. You are each an inspiration to the Lyme community.

Thank you to my team, who worked diligently to support the assembled of this book in record time- organizing interviews with global time zones, last minute formatting edits, cover design, and working with my high energy and wild ideas. I could not have put this book together without them. Thank you to the Global Lyme Alliance (GLA) for your support and collaboration in sharing the most recent research and education on Lyme Disease.

A final thank you to my kids, who inspire me daily. They are the true reason I wrote this book to bring greater global awareness of Lyme Disease. I will continue to work towards a cure or better a world free of Lyme for all.

"I never find sincerity offensive...
so, be sincere."

- Christopher Meloni

Forward

CHRISTOPHER MELONI

New York, NY

Intense. Funny. Committed.

Most of us are told a simple story about Lyme, if we are told one at all. It goes something like this: "if a tick bites you, probably nothing will happen. BUT if you see the telltale red bullseye on your skin then take antibiotics and you'll be fine". End of story. Simple. Straight forward. They lived happily ever after. Get on with life. Well...that narrative may fit sometimes; it may fit most of the time, but when it doesn't, then the story is long, unending, and complicated; a happy ending seems impossible and "getting on with life" is a Sisyphean endeavor.

The truth about Lyme disease is that it is dangerously mis-understood by the public and often misdiagnosed by doc-tors. Although it is one of the fastest growing epidemics in America, research is grossly underfunded. In fact there are some medical institutions that still refuse to recognize chronic or persistent Lyme disease as a real condition.

Lyme is extraordinarily complicated. It can come with a host of different infectious bacterium, each of which can manifest itself differently in each individual and thus bring with it any number of the over 300 symptoms that often mimic other diseases-a diagnosis of arthritis, multiple sclerosis, neuropathy, and even dementia may be made when the real culprit is chronic Lyme.

I've seen what it can do to people- people I love. I've seen the grinding pain in the joints, muscles, and head. I've stood helplessly by and watched the daily routine of vomiting, brain fog, and fatigue that turns people into bed ridden torture victims.

Everything about Lyme disease is complicated and often fraught with misinformation, frustration, and suffering. This is where Kenzie Vath comes in. The Ignored Pandemic: Real Stories of Lyme Disease is a concise introduction into all aspects of Lyme. It gives you an overview of the history and the science of Lyme, the problems those who suffer from it face and also those who are fighting the "system" to get the medical community to pay attention.

And most importantly in these pages are the stories. Hear the voices of not victims, but of warriors. Go on the journeys of those who suffer, endure, and fight every day. Read the truth.

What should you do with Lyme

Make LymeAid

Preface

Suicide felt like the only option.

To write my story and truly portray the indescribable fight of Lyme Disease. I had to go to a place I promised myself I would never go. Welcome thoughts into my head that I have worked tirelessly to erase, and a daily reminder of obsessive thinking patterns I had to rewire.

Most, if not all of us, have had the moment retreating to the fetal position crying on the bathroom floor. The feeling of complete loneliness. In that single moment you reflect on what shakes you to the core. For me, it was the isolation from my peers and family while trying to explain my struggle and still not being heard. The consistent trend of being misunderstood. The chronic pain I was not able to treat, due to the lack of interest, and awareness from my physicians. I was done.

Feeling these intense emotions is part of what makes us human. But that emotional feeling can be at times unbearable. When your emotions overcome your ability to reason and have purpose; fear presents itself. The lowest and darkest point in my life was the fear of my future. I was beyond tired of asking for help, looking for answers, misunderstood, completely written off, and ignored. I felt worthless, empty, meaningless, isolated, garbage taking up space in this life. Truly no purpose. For me the absence of purpose convinced my thoughts there was no reason to live.

What did I do next? I had to fight my thoughts daily. My obsession with suicide and how to end my life painlessly cannibalized my thoughts. I wanted the pain and suffering to end. Begging God, every night before bed, "Please don't let me wake up...."

I am writing this book for all who suffer in silence looking for answers and asking to be heard. After ten years of searching and fighting I received my diagnosis of Lyme Disease. Finally, relieved to have an answer for the former ten years of suffering, but unaware of the next ten-year journey of unbearable treatment. There were moments I did not think I would make it through.

Yet, I have conquered the odds and fought the mental battle of ending my life. I know my story and the collection of stories from Lyme Warriors in this book will bring hope to those suffering and validating you are not alone.

Please, read this book to educate yourself about Lyme Disease and tick-borne illness. Lyme disease is the fastest growing vector illness in the United States. It's an ignored pandemic and we collectively need to come together to make noise and create change. Get educated and become more aware of the life-altering illnesses that lurk in our backyard.

CONTENT

Part One : Get Educated

Part Two : Stories

Introduction

Lyme Disease: The Ignored Pandemic

Lyme disease is a bacterial infection caused by the spirochete bacterium Borrelia burgdorferi. Currently, the most common transmission to humans is through a bite from infected black-legged ticks. However, there has been an increased number of studies regarding the transition of Lyme disease from other vector animals.

A vector animal is an insect, rodent, bird, or other creature that carries disease pathogens; this could include a human. As many know, the most common vector insects are ticks and mosquitoes. Lyme disease was first identified in the United States in the town of Lyme, Connecticut, in the 1970s, and has since spread to many other parts of the world.

In recent years, Lyme disease has become a growing public health concern globally, with reported cases increasing in many countries, included but not limited to the United States, Canada, Australia, and Europe. According to the World Health Organization (WHO), Lyme disease is the most common tick-borne disease in the Northern Hemisphere and is estimated to affect hundreds of thousands of people worldwide every year.

The actual number of cases is much higher due to underdiagnosis and misdiagnosis patients, as the many symptoms of Lyme disease can mimic those of several other illnesses and disease. Many Lyme warriors experience a handful of diagnoses before they are ever tested for Lyme or other tick-borne infections. You will get a glimpse of these various misdiagnoses in the interview to come. Particular common misdiagnoses include: Fibromyalgia; Chronic Fatigue Syndrome; Multiple Sclerosis (MS); Lupus; and Rheumatoid Arthritis.

Many countries lack proper surveillance systems to accurately track the incidence of Lyme disease. Without proper tracking, it will continue to spread in vast numbers beyond what is reported.

Given the increasing incidence of Lyme disease and the challenges in accurately diagnosing and treating the disease. There is a growing need for greater public awareness, improved diagnostic tools, and more effective treatments. The WHO has called for additional research and collaboration on a global scale to address the public health impact of Lyme disease.

To assist with this noble mission, this book will cover the basics of Lyme disease, with a focus on raising awareness, identify symptoms and signs of a tick bite, Lyme disease prevention and reducing exposure, as well as the various stages of Lyme, diagnosis and treatment options, research and testing, and other critical factors. My hope is that the book will provide you with more information about this growing pandemic, so you can protect yourself and your loved ones from Lyme Disease.

It is only with further education and research that we will be able to arrive at better solutions for Lyme disease testing and treatment, prevention, and monitoring. Whether you have a personal or professional interest in Lyme disease, I'm confident you will find value and new insight in the pages ahead.

Part One

Get Educated

CHAPTER 01

Lyme Disease

The Often-Invisible Illness

People who contract Lyme disease have a difficult time getting a diagnosis. When they do, it's often after months, and sometimes years, of struggle and emotional turmoil. You know when something is wrong. You can tell when your body isn't "right." But when you can't get to the root of what's causing it, much less get doctors to listen to your concerns, it can be devastating.

The symptoms of Lyme are vast and varied, and when the disease doesn't present right away with a bulls-eye rash and flu-like symptoms; the chronic symptoms can become difficult to connect to the disease. For example, some chronic Lyme patients experience extreme fatigue, memory loss, stiff joints, sore throat, and other flu-like symptoms, without ever being diagnosed with Lyme.

At first glance, these symptoms could be caused by any number of conditions. It's no wonder doctors don't jump straight to a Lyme diagnosis. Later in this book, we're going to look at the stories of people who have been through Lyme or are currently dealing with it, most of whom have (or had) chronic conditions. What you'll notice in all these stories is a common thread: misdiagnoses and a misunderstood illness that often leads to fear, frustration, and a feeling of isolation.

So, let me say this first. If you or someone you love is dealing with Lyme, struggling to get answers, or having a hard time finding a doctor to listen to, keep fighting. Keep advocating. Keep looking for help and never stop questioning. The answers are out there, And most importantly, you are absolutely not alone.

Why Does Lyme Get Missed So Often?

There are several potential reasons that Lyme disease gets overlooked as a diagnosis, starting with the sheer lack of information and awareness about how prevalent and serious the disease actually is. There is also the fact that despite the Infectious Diseases Society of America deeming antibiotics to be an effective treatment for Lyme, many people continue to have chronic symptoms like neuropathy, brain fog, digestive issues, muscle and joint pain (all of which are also easily related to dozens of other illnesses and conditions).

Often symptoms present themselves internally and are not externally visible to a physician or others. So patients get written off or ignored, many being told to go home and rest from what people think is stress. Symptoms are not commonly linked to chronic Lyme unless the physician or patient is fortunate to know what Lyme disease is. There are Lyme-literate physicians in the medical field who specialize in Lyme and tick-borne disease. It is always recommended that a patient seek support from an expert; they are well-educated on the disease. Many patients only seek support from a Lyme-literate doctor after years of misdisgnosis or ineffective treatment. Then comes the challenge of finding one near you and getting in. Unfortunately, there are very few Lyme-literate physicians in the market today and may have waitlists that extend months. All the while, we as patients are struggling to stay sane and keep functioning, amid often debilitating symptoms.

The majority of patients who have dealt with chronic illness will tell you the same thing: it is beyond discouraging to battle debilitating symptoms while navigating through the medical system without answers. Patients become a number, passed from one doctor to the next. The lucky ones have health care providers who listen and believe them and fight alongside them. The others fight alone, isolated, passed on, and ignored. They don't understand or believe their condition. When no answer appears in the labs, scans, etc. they move on.

This is part of why I do what I do, and why so many others in the Lyme community advocate, as well. We need more research, resources, and funding directed toward a better understanding of Lyme disease. The more we share our stories confidently and speak up, the brighter and healthier our future will be.

The Struggle of Living with an Invisible Illness

People who have Lyme can face insurmountable challeng-es. That includes the challenge of living with a condition that's essentially "invisible" to most people and "claimed" nonexistent in many countries. It causes feelings of judgment, shame, isolation, frustration, anger, depression, suicidal tendencies, and more. It also brings a lot of fear due to the uncertainty and worry about what others think.

As you will learn throughout this book, or as those who have (or have had) Lyme disease know firsthand, the symptoms of this disease aren't always visible and can't always be accurately diagnosed. Even those who do have Lyme may have good days where they "seem fine" even though they're still battling their disease underneath. But many of those supposedly "good days" could be just getting out of bed. The bad days look different for everyone, but the majority isolate themselves from the world, cooped up in bed unable to even perform a simple task like going to the bathroom. It's an ongoing cycle of starving for energy and trying to get answers. When you are sick, it is a struggle to articulate what you are dealing with. And most of the time, people don't even believe you.

With Lyme, there are other elements that create a challenge:

The unique manifestations of the illness.

The political climate globally: There are countries that claim Lyme disease does not exist and will not allow any educational material about Lyme to be published in their country and doctors are not allowed to treat Lyme.

Being gas-lighted by most of the medical community.

The rollercoaster of every changing symptoms.

The uncertainty surrounding diagnosis and treatment.

The psychological effects of feeling invalidated and facing an "invisible" illness.

The lack of appropriate funding for more research to find better diagnostic tools, treatments, and hopefully, one day, a cure.

Questions and External Judgments

It can be challenging to deal with a condition like Lyme disease because you feel this constant need to prove that there is, in fact, something wrong with you. The current testing methods result in many false negatives, and that's only if doctors arrive at the conclusion that Lyme may be involved in the first place. This process is draining. It leads to self-doubt and feelings of insecurity, often fueling depression, anxiety, and a desire to isolate because no one understands what you're going through- or worse, no one believes that you're sick. Many I have spoken with start to doubt themselves: what if this isn't real, what if I really am making this up? I highly recommend watching the documentary; *I'm Not Crazy, I'm Sick*, by Director Elle Ginter. It gives you a better understanding of the emotions of those who suffer in silence.

The best advice that I can give to anyone with a chronic illness is never give up! Regarding the judgment and questions of others, be your own advocate. Not only will this help you educate the public one person at a time, but it will give you the confidence to speak up and speak out and say, "Yes, I am sick, even if you can't see it."

Chronic Fatigue, Brain Fog, and Mental Challenges

The next set of obstacles faced by those with chronic illnesses are internal, and usually mental in nature. Lyme, like many chronic illnesses, is characterized by chronic fatigue and issues with mental clarity. Memory troubles, brain fog, and struggles with motivation are no joke. They can lead to additional frustration or anger about being ill, even if people are aware that they're experiencing symptoms of an illness and not just "forgetful", "stupid," or "lazy."

Chronic pain and joint issues that are commonly found in those who have Lyme. Living in a state of constant pain and discomfort takes a huge toll on your daily life. It affects your emotional and mental well-being, as well as your physical health, and it often prevents you from enjoying the things you used to love most. For some of us, it has eliminated the ability to participate in our favorite activities and even maintain a career. Pain alters our emotional response and reaction to people. Pain is linked to anger, anxiety, and depression- difficulties you may again not be able to see, but greatly affect your quality of life.

Guilt and Shame

Lyme brings with it a healthy dose of guilt and a sense of being a burden to others. Some people feel embarrassed when they experience symptoms that they can't explain or that they have no answers for. Others are frustrated and ashamed that they can't remember people's names or other simple details in conversation. Still more feel guilty that they have this condition that is taking such a toll on their caretakers, family, friends, and others, both emotionally and financially.

If you ask anyone with a chronic illness, they'll tell you that they've heard the phrase "you don't look sick to me", more times than they can count. We know we don't look sick. In fact, it's one of the biggest struggles for most chronic illness sufferers, whether they have Lyme or another condition. This can lead to even more guilt, as it starts to feel like it's all our fault, we're letting people down, and that we "just can't do" what everyone else can. Lyme patients often live in silos. They don't share their story out of shame and they lose friends when battling the illness and treatment process.

Some people feel the burden on their families financially since insurance does not cover most treatment options currently available for Lyme. Some of these treatments include: IV therapy; ozone therapy; stem cell therapy; herbal remedies; FMT; and others that are not FDA-approved or specifically directed for the treatment of Lyme disease. They usually require payment out-of-pocket for those who seek them out.

All told, the challenges of invisible illness can lead to many feelings of guilt and shame, and they can start to build up quickly if they aren't dealt with. Speaking of which, let's talk a little about how to overcome these challenges.

How to Overcome These (and Other) Challenges

If you are someone who has been diagnosed with Lyme disease, or any chronic illness for that matter, you are inevitably going to come across many challenges in your journey to find the right treatment. Part of the reason why so many people don't get the help they need is because they keep hitting a wall. They eventually give up before getting answers.

Don't give up - that's probably the absolute best piece of advice and last option for Lyme patients. And while it's easier said than done, this resilience and determination that will help you overcome the obstacles on your journey. In addition to staying the course, there are some other ways you can meet these challenges head on:

Find your tribe. Lean on supportive friends, family, and fellow Lymies.

Let go of the guilt. You have an illness and you did not choose it. You should not feel bad about that.

Know your limits. But don't sell yourself short.

Pick your battles. Whether it's work, advocacy, or treatment routines, evaluate whether things are worth your time and energy- because you know energy is like gold.

Keep a journal. Tracking your journey and the small accomplishments will help once you start to break out of the darkness.

Spread awareness. Share your story and advocate for yourself and others. This is the best way to inform people and alleviate your own embarrassment by getting rid of the stigma.

It's not easy, but it's worth the effort. Especially when dealing with a condition like Lyme disease or another chronic illness, you must give yourself space and be your own voice because no one else is going to do it for you. It helps if you also have the support of family and friends.

Speaking of which, if you're among that group (family, friends, and caretakers), let's take a look at how you can help your loved one navigate and manage their invisible illness.

Support From Family, Friends, and Caretakers

Most of the people that I've encountered in the Lyme community want one thing more than anything else: supportive family, friends, and caretakers to help them through this difficult and uncertain time. When you are seeing dozens of doctors, getting a handful of diagnoses, treatment suggestions, lists of medication, and supplements, yet still not getting the relief you need it can be defeating and disheartening. It's at times like these that people need support more than anything.

If you know someone who has Lyme disease or another invisible illness, be kind. Be supportive and listen. Ask how you can help, what they need, and be aware that not everyone is going to be so kind to them. It could be attending a doctor's appointment with them and taking notes since the information is overwhelming if you're sick. Drop off a home-cooked meal at their home, since making a meal for yourself can be exhausting and many don't bother to even eat. It can be as simple as sending a text message: "You are strong, you got this!" Advocate for them with the medical community, as well as with the public. Help spread awareness of invisible illnesses to the forefront of everyone's mind.

At the same time, make sure that you're not becoming an advocate for someone who doesn't need or want it. If you have someone in your life who prefers to keep their condition private, let them have that. Follow the lead of whoever you're supporting and you will always know how to give them exactly what they need.

We're Not Crazy

Finally, I want to reiterate one more time for anyone who is still feeling uncertain or overwhelmed by what they are facing: you are not crazy. We are not crazy. No one is "making up" having Lyme disease or another chronic illness. You can't fake chronic fatigue. You can't fake debilitating joint issues, neuropathy, brain fog and memory issues, and the many other symptoms of Lyme.

Whatever you're feeling, wherever you are in your Lyme experience, it is real and valid and true. Keep fighting to find doctors who will listen and support you and help you get the right treatment. If you encounter people who try to write you off, send you for a psych consult, or diagnose you with whatever chronic illness is trending that week just to get you off the agenda, find other people.

They are out there. It just might take some time for you to find them. In the meantime, know that you're not crazy, and you are absolutely not alone. If I can do anything besides educating more people about Lyme with this book, that would be it: to let anyone at any stage in their illness know that they are not alone, no matter how isolated or outcast they feel by whatever they are going through.

Now, let's get to know Lyme disease.

CHAPTER 02

Lyme Basics

Get to know the Disease

It's the 21st century, which often leads people to wrongly assume that conditions like Lyme disease, "aren't really an issue" anymore. You don't hear as much about this disease because it's far more isolated and disconnected than in the past.

However, there are an estimated 476,000 new cases of Lyme disease diagnosed every year. Reminder: you can get Lyme multiple times. Even if you've been bitten once, you can always get bitten again.

Taking the time to understand this disease, its symptoms, and how to prevent it can save countless people from developing a life altering disease. But first we must answer: what exactly is Lyme disease and where does it come from?

When the doctor was telling us about the tick-borne disease called Lyme, they weren't talking about the citrus fruit. Lyme disease can be frightening in and of itself, but I also know that the ghost of not knowing why your health is struggling will always be far more frightening. In that vein, I hope these pages can help empower you to move through that uncertainty and fear. Find hope through empowering yourself with information on prevention, treatment options, and sympathizing with a Lyme warrior. There is life to be had with Lyme.

What Is Lyme?

Despite nearly half a million new reported cases per year and climbing, Lyme disease remains ignored and misunderstood by the general public- and, some would debate, even more by the medical community. Some outside of the medical community consider it to be nothing more than a rash, perhaps an allergic reaction to a tick bite that will heal on its own. Two weeks of antibiotics and you'll be cured, the argument goes.

The reality is that Lyme disease is an incredibly complex condition that seems to manifest itself differently in each person it infects. It leads to a wide variety of symptoms, some more noticeable than others. Symptoms might not be concerning at first, then suddenly, you're debilitated. In fact, there are so many symptoms that it can often be difficult to be positive that the problem is Lyme disease and thus not the first diagnosis physicians will jump to test. Traditionally, a textbook Lyme has a bullseye rash present where the tick bite was, followed by flu-like symptoms. Prescription would be given for two weeks of doxycycline. Yet the majority of the time, Acute Lyme is not diagnosed or rapidly treated leading to Chronic Lyme disease.

Lyme disease is caused by a bacteria known as Borrelia burgdorferi, not an easy one to say; or less often Borrelia mayonii. This spiral-shaped, stretchy bacteria most commonly infects humans through Deer ticks and Black-legged ticks. But this is not always the case.

Recently, new findings have indicated that Lyme disease is capable of being transmitted through any vector that excretes DNA into the body. Furthermore, the CDC says that new research shows that untreated Lyme disease can be transmitted in utero. Thus, this condition is classified as an infectious disease.

The History of Lyme Disease in the U.S.

Lyme disease was first discovered in the United States in Lyme, Connecticut, in the early 1970s. There was an outbreak that affected a significant group of children and adults, who all had a host of puzzling symptoms that became quite debilitating. Symptoms included but were not limited to skin rashes, headaches, swollen knees, paralysis, and severe chronic fatigue.

Most families were left without a diagnosis or any treatment during the better part of the 1960s and 1970s as this disease was first becoming known. Two mothers from the Connecticut outbreak were insistent that doctors look for answers, reach out to scientists, and find more information. Medical professionals started to study the children and adults affected by this outbreak. Since the children had all reported skin rashes and similar arthritic ailments, along with reporting a tick bite in the Lyme area, it was determined they were all suffering from what they dubbed Lyme disease.

Of course, there was still little known about the actual cause of the condition. The fact that all those affected had been bitten by ticks was some indication, but ticks carry dozens, if not hundreds, of potentially dangerous bacteria and diseases. Therefore, more research was needed.

Willy Burgdorfer, a Swiss American Scientist, was studying Rocky Mountain Spotted Fever in 1981. He then switched gears to study Lyme disease. It wasn't long before he found the connection between deer ticks and Lyme. He discovered that a bacterium carried by ticks was responsible for causing this disease. For his discovery, he was honored in 1982 when they named the bacterium after him: Borrelia burgdorferi.

Recent History and Today

The incidence of Lyme disease has increased significantly since the 1980s. In the early 2000s, there was a growing global concern with a focus on the U.S. outbreaks and in 2012, the CDC included Lyme disease on the top 10 list of notifiable diseases.

Lyme disease is currently one of the fastest-growing infections that is vector-borne (as of now with the vector being the tick) and although it remains more prevalent on the East Coast, Lyme has been reported in every state with the exception of Hawaii. Despite the explosion of cases, current diagnostic and testing tools are unreliable and there is still no definite cure for people who have late-stage Lyme disease.

Lyme Disease Outbreaks/Cases – Areas at Risk

Different parts of the county have different levels of risk. Currently, the greatest risk of Lyme disease is found in the Northeastern U.S., running from Minnesota to Maine and then down to North Carolina.

There is a moderate risk of Lyme disease across the entire eastern U.S. The West Coast is also at higher risk than the rest of the country because of the increased population of the Western Deer Tick. If you live in any of these areas, get any tick that bites you (or a loved one) tested for Lyme. Have the tests repeated in two weeks to be sure.

Keep in mind the increase of infection will grow outside of this 'hot bed'. Lyme disease has seen a significant increase due to environmental changes. A good book on Lyme and the environment is called, "Lyme: The First Epidemic of Climate Change" by Mary Jane Pfeiffer.

Symptoms and What to Look For

Lyme disease is known to have a variety of symptoms, causing confusion for many medical professionals and leading to frequent misdiagnosis. Some people may experience a few onset symptoms, while others may experience more severe and life treating symptoms. There are even cases where people may not have many symptoms at all aside from the trademark bullseye rash. Symptoms are also defined as early-stage or acute onset and late-stage or chronic symptoms.

The Rash

This is the classic symptom of Lyme disease. Formally known as Erythema migrans, the rash is initially centered around the bite. With time, the rash spreads outward. At the same time, the middle starts to heal and the actual bite site will remain unaffected, creating that familiar bullseye shape. Crucially, the rash only presents itself roughly 60-70 percent of the time.

Early-Stage Symptoms

These are the symptoms that are experienced in the first 30 days after the initial tick bite. Some of the symptoms seen in these early stages of Lyme include:

- Fever
- Brain fog
- Chills
- Headache and body aches
- Rashes (including the rash at the bite site)
- Fatigue

Late-Stage Symptoms

Those suffering from more advanced Lyme disease (that has been undiagnosed for weeks to months after a tick bite) may experience the following:

- Severe headaches
- Neck stiffness
- Additional severe rashes throughout the body
- Intermittent joint, bone, and muscle pain
- Arthritis with joint swelling and pain
- Facial palsy

- Nerve pain
- Heart palpitations
- Shortness of breath
- Dizziness
- Numbness and pain in the hands and feet

Mental Health Symptoms and Concerns

Patients who are diagnosed with Lyme disease often report a range of symptoms related to mental health. Some have anxiety and panic attacks that can last for hours or feel constantly anxious in their everyday lives. Others report issues with brain fog, including difficulty concentrating and focusing, trouble tracking words when reading, and more. It can be frustrating, to say the least.

Still more patients have been diagnosed with depression or anxiety conditions and are completely unaware that they were bitten by a tick and may be infected with Lyme disease. In extreme cases, some people develop auditory hallucinations, such as hearing a radio that isn't on or music when there is none.

Lorraine Johnson, now the chief executive officer (CEO) of LymeDisease.org, was diagnosed in the early 1990s with major depression. This was in response to severe changes in concentration, mood, and thinking. She was treated with psychotropic medications with no benefit and spent about five years trying to figure out where things went wrong.

None of the medications worked. There was no family history of mental illness and she had never had symptoms like this before. However, after much struggle, Johnson was finally able to get diagnosed with Lyme disease. That was followed by two years of medical treatment that included antibiotics and other therapies. Surprisingly, the depressive symptoms disappeared, and she has not had any further issues with her mood since.

Because of her own experience, she became an advocate and now leads one of the major Lyme Disease initiatives in the country. The bottom line here is that misdiagnosis can lead to a lot of concerns for mental health patients.

Mental health providers have been sharing patient cases with Lyme disease doctors, helping drive research and making physicians more aware that people are also experiencing depression, anxiety, and other mental health issues alongside their Lyme diagnosis. But this does not happen nearly enough. Such efforts help clinicians and researchers alike factor in all the potential symptoms, including things like light and sound sensitivity, numbness and tingling, cognitive issues, and more.

Lyme-Based Anxiety

In the 1990s, it was discovered that Lyme-driven anxiety and mental illnesses were a serious concern. Many people were being referred for treatment for hypochondria, even though they didn't have a previous history of mental illness, including anxiety or related conditions. These patients also reported symptoms like fatigue, joint pain, cognitive issues, and other Lyme-type symptoms. Eventually, it was discovered that the anxiety came from Lyme disease, which warrants much more study in the future.

People who have had Lyme disease also report that they never had issues with anxiety or depression until after they were affected with the condition. Recent studies have shown that those who have Lyme disease are 28 percent more likely to be diagnosed with anxiety or another mental health disorder. So, there is proof that there is a connection between the Lyme bacteria and mental health, including case studies that have shown patients developing conditions and symptoms like:

- Anxiety
- Panic attacks
- Depression
- Depressive episodes
- Manic episodes
- Auditory and visual hallucinations

There could be other symptoms present, but these are the most common that people experience when having Lyme-based mental health issues.

Most of the patients being studied are ill enough to be diagnosed in a hospital setting, either during outpatient psychiatric care or during the admission process. Mind you, this study is not focused on typical Lyme patients, but those who have contracted a severe form of the condition and who have extreme symptoms that have resulted in the need for hospitalization and other treatments. Many Lyme patients suffering from mental illness are never validated for their symptoms or condition. They are not properly diagnosed and often lead to a life of pharmaceuticals and chronic suffering.

Moreover, people who are adjusting to life with Lyme disease and its debilitating effects can feel a strain on their mental health. People often have to limit daily activities or change their lifestyle because of chronic pain and fatigue, which can be taxing in and of itself. Some people hide the seriousness of their condition because people don't believe, support, or understand them. Many if not most lack support from their primary care providers.

Diagnosis

The diagnosis of Lyme disease is usually done through laboratory testing, although some physical signs and symptoms could be good indicators that the condition is present. Doctors need to consider those symptoms, as well as:

- The possibility that there's another illness with similar symptoms.
- The likelihood that the individual has been exposed to infected ticks.
- The results of laboratory tests, once completed.

If you have been bitten by a tick and are capable of doing so, keep the tick so that you can present it to the doctor to assist with the determination of your case. It can also help notify local authorities of a potential local tick disease outbreak.

The CDC recommends a two-step test that utilizes a blood sample. The first test will either test negative, positive, or indeterminate. If it is negative, no further testing is required. If the first test comes back indeterminate or positive, the second test should be performed. The diagnosis of Lyme disease is only determined to be "positive" if both tests are positive or equivocal, depending on other symptoms and circumstances.

There is also ongoing support for the development of new tests or more efficient testing methods. They must be approved by the FDA, of course, but the CDC welcomes medical experts to reach out with their new testing methods and concepts in the hope to find a better way to diagnose Lyme disease and similar conditions.

The majority of Lyme disease tests are based on the detection of antibodies that have been created to respond to the infection. These can take several weeks to fully develop, which means negative tests early on will be common. However, antibodies can persist for several months or even years once the infection has cleared, which means it can't be used to determine whether the disease is cured.

Those who have other conditions like autoimmune diseases, viral and bacterial conditions, and tick-borne diseases will find that they may get false positives due to other infections in the body.

Lyme Prevention

There are several strategies and tips to assist with the prevention of Lyme disease. The most obvious is to avoid being bitten by a tick. Some areas are "tick infested," putting you at higher risk of a tick bite and not ever seeing the tick to begin with. The book is intended to educate the lay consumer on the danger of Lyme disease and other tick-borne infections, and the following resources can help.

A.W.A.R.E.

A.W.A.R.E. is an acronym developed by the Global Lyme Alliance in 2017, as part of their tick bite prevention program. It stands for:

- AVOID high-traffic areas for ticks, like leaf piles, tall grass, and wooded areas.
- WEAR proper clothing, including socks, long sleeves,

and long pants.
- APPLY an eco-friendly tick repellant to discourage their bites.
- REMOVE clothing when you get home and place it in a hot dryer (do not wash clothing, go straight to HOT dryer)
- EXAMINE yourself for ticks regularly.

Ultimately, the goal is to make prevention easy so that people will be less likely to face tick-borne diseases like Lyme. As a secondary part of this program, the GLA also introduced a great visual reference on where to check for ticks to make sure that you don't miss anything:

BE TICK AWARE

 A Avoid areas where ticks live. Ticks thrive in wood piles, long grass, leaf piles and beach grass.

 W Wear light-colored clothing; long pants, sleeves, socks and close-toed shoes.

 A Apply EPA-approved tick repellent (such as DEET or picaridin) to skin and insecticide (such as permethrin) to clothing and shoes as directed.

 R Remove clothing upon entering the home; toss into dryer at HIGH temperature for 10-15 minutes.

 E Examine yourself and your pets for ticks daily. Check everywhere--ticks love to hide!

Learn about ticks, Lyme and other tick-borne diseases, tick bite prevention and proper tick removal at GLA.org

 **GLOBAL LYME ALLIANCE**

They have a #BeTickAWARE campaign online to promote tick awareness and Lyme disease prevention, as well.

Length of Attachment

The sooner you notice a tick, the quicker you should properly remove it. According to the CDC, a tick must be attached to a person for at least 36 to 48 hours before the bacteria can be transmitted to the body. However this is not the case. We now know many of the tick-borne illnesses can be transmitted within 15 mins. There is no grace period when it comes to infection. As one article state, " many pathogens in the Rickettsia family, like Rocky Mountain spotted fever, can be deadly if not treated within the first few days" (snowden, 2022). Scientific articles have debunked the CDC's claim and its false sense of security that you are unable to get Lyme if a tick is not on the body for 36 hours. This is simply not true.

Regular tick checks must be done even in areas where you may think Lyme does not exist. If your kids are playing out in the fields or running in the backyard, then tick checks should be mandatory. It's not worth taking the risk and losing your life over this illness. The most common reason for the increase of Lyme disease in today's society is the lack of education. People are not paying attention or noticing a tick until it's too late. That's why the GLA and others have worked to create so many awareness and prevention campaigns.

We'll talk more about ticks and their pesky ways of embedding into your skin in the next chapter.

Landscaping and Lawn Treatments

For people living in regions where tick populations are high, prevention is a big part of daily life. In hot bed areas parents are checking their kids and dogs for ticks when they come up from playing out on the lawn. They know what lies within the grass and brush. Many seek out landscaping solutions and lawn treatments that are designed to deter or eliminate ticks. This, in turn, reduces ticks in the backyard decreasing the likelihood of being bitten by an infected tick.

The Centers for Disease Control (CDC) does provide an infographic on how to make your yard or outdoor spaces less appealing to ticks and other pests. If you are specifically trying to deter ticks from settling down in your yard or the areas around your home, here's what you need to know.

- Clear all tall brush and grasses around the home, including those further away from the structures.
- Keep leaves raked and mow the lawn regularly to prevent ticks from settling in.
- Place a three-foot barrier of gravel or wood chips between lawns and wooded areas, around patios, and play equipment. This can keep ticks from migrating into your yard.
- Keep all patios, decks, and playground equipment in the sun and away from the edge of the lawn when possible.
- Remove all trash and debris from the yard that may provide hiding spots to harbor ticks.
- Apply *pesticides to your yard to reduce the number of ticks present.

*I personally do not recommend pesticides since we know they are also harmful to our health. Luckily mother nature has provided some great alternative options. There has been an increase of popularity in essential oil options to ward off ticks including: Thyme; Oregano; Eucalyptus; and Clove, to name a few. I am also a fan of the Wondercide brand for backyards and pets.

Speaking of those pesky ticks, now that we've covered the basics of Lyme disease, let's take a closer look at the ticks that cause it.

CHAPTER 03

Know Your Ticks

From their Lifecycles to the Removal

Education and awareness are a big part of preventing Lyme disease. To that end, it's also helpful to have a better knowledge and understanding of ticks themselves, including the ones that cause the majority of disease, when they are most likely to be out, and other factors.

To many people including myself, ticks are little alien creatures that are terrifying, to say the least. They are smaller than most ants and many other bugs, but we know they can cause life altering disease, which is why understanding the tick is such an important part of reducing infections and illness rates.

The Tick Lifecycle: Growing Up as a Blood Feeder

Ticks have a two- to three-year lifecycle, similar to most arthropods (arachnids and insects). At each stage of their life, they must be able to feed on blood or they will die. Gross, right? Death happens to many ticks at every stage of the lifecycle. But it's not enough to disrupt their reproduction or their population rates. After all, most adult females lay 1,500 to 5,000 eggs at a time. That is a lot of baby ticks, basically creating a tick army.

Whenever a tick feeds, there's a chance that it will pick up some type of infection. That infection can be transmitted to every future host, including humans. Some pathogens infect certain species and can even infect eggs while they are in utero. Ticks are no laughing matter.

While many people think of deer or their beloved dogs when it comes to ticks, birds are also popular hosts. Not only can they provide a place to feed, but they can travel with the tick and take it to an area where there is less saturation and more food.

Eggs and Larva

Ticks lay their eggs in the late winter and early spring, which will hatch toward the end of spring to create larval ticks that look like poppyseeds to many. They will immediately start looking for hosts and remain active into the summer and fall months. Many will begin to die out, while others will go dormant. At this time, their hosts are reptiles and small birds. They are too small to infect a human and most small mammals, so they will feed on smaller creatures to prepare and grow into the next stage.

Nymphs

Nymphs will develop two more legs, bringing the total to eight, but they still won't be able to reproduce. They feed on birds and small mammals and they can choose from a variety of hosts at this point. They usually stick to smaller animals for easy penetration, but they will continue to grow in their host search, looking for increasingly more blood to feed on over time.

These ticks will take 10 minutes to two hours to fully attach to a human host. These ticks are also the size of a poppyseed and can be invisible to the human eye- just a speck of black. Unlike the larvae, these ticks will continue to find hosts throughout the year as they need them. However, nymphs also struggle to tolerate the cold so they will be most active in the spring and summer months.

Adult Ticks

Adult ticks are fully ready to reproduce and at their largest size, which means they can implant themselves in many small mammals and humans. Ticks become adults around the fall of their third year. They will last until the middle of spring, and then begin to die off. Some will make it to summer, but this is generally the end of the line for ticks.

Adult females are larger than males, even before feeding. That's necessary for all the eggs that she will be laying in the coming months. Their hosts at this stage include larger mammals, birds, and humans, and these ticks will be much more difficult to remove once they are embedded in the skin.

Questing and Feeding

When ticks are searching for a host, it is a process referred to as "questing". They will climb onto tall grasses or other high locations where they will be likely to brush against a potential host. Once they are positioned, they will reach their legs out to attach to the host as it is passing. Questing is also triggered by several different signals, including:

- Nearby movement
- Increases in heat
- Rising carbon dioxide levels

Ticks are smart and have several ways of finding a host. They know that once they have climbed aboard, they need to find a good place to hide. They usually seek out the hairline, behind the ears, and other skin folds or areas where they might not be noticed. This will allow them to feed uninterrupted.

The unique thing about tick bites is that when they embed themselves in a host, they often also release an analgesic that ensures the host doesn't feel the actual "bite" and won't try to remove the tick right away. Some ticks also apply chemicals that inhibit the immune response or reduce swelling to help increase blood flow, and there are even ticks that use a type of self-produced cement to keep themselves in place.

Ticks have a mouthpart that grabs and holds the skin, while another part known as the hypostome will use its barbs to penetrate the skin and create what is known as the feeding cavity. They create and cultivate this cavity by injecting and consuming their own saliva, helping to expand the void. Once the cavity has reached a good size, the tick will expel its stomach contents. This is when almost all infections happen.

Some research has shown this process to take hours to days, depending on the species of tick and its stage of life. If the tick can be removed before this entire process occurs, the infection risk can be reduced. Again, that's why regular checks and awareness are such an integral part of preventing Lyme disease and other tick-borne infections.

Where are Ticks Located?

Based on a simple google search; Ticks can be found throughout the entire United States, but they are more common in some areas than others. The type of tick that causes Lyme is known as the black-legged tick or the Western black-legged tick, and it is most commonly found in the Eastern U.S. The populations are higher in coastal states like North and South Carolina, Connecticut, and Florida, but areas with a lot of wooded space, like New York, Pennsylvania, Ohio, and Kentucky, all see their fair share of ticks, too. However, if you dive into the research you find that ticks are found all over the world, even on the beaches of southern California. The second part of this book show-cases a handful of stories from Lyme warriors who were infected outside of the US.

The Western black-legged tick is found on the West Coast in states like Oregon, Washington, and California. It is less prevalent than its East Coast sibling, but this population is seeing growth, as well. Therefore, everyone should make sure that they know whether they're at risk based on where they live and how to best protect themselves from the dangers that come from crossing paths with a tick, including Lyme disease.

Several other species of ticks carry a plethora of other diseases and health issues that don't have a connection to Lyme disease even though many would say they fall under the umbrella of Lyme. There are a few ticks known for causing Rocky Mountain Spotted Fever, for example, but that's usually only seen in the Rocky Mountain region of the United States. However, cases have been increasing outside of the Rockies and presenting itself in Lyme infected ticks.

Infections Caused by Ticks

As mentioned above, ticks can transmit several diseases in addition to Lyme disease. There are a variety of symptoms and conditions that may be the result of a tick bite or having a tick embedded in the skin. Let's take a closer look at some of those here.

Anaplasmosis

Anaplasmosis is a condition that is caused by a bacterium known as Anaplasma Phagocytophilum. The bacteria that cause this condition are carried by the same tick that carries Lyme, the black-legged tick or black-legged deer tick. Anaplasmosis can affect humans and pets, with symptoms appearing within one to two weeks of being infected by a tick. Depending on how long the body has been infected, this condition can create different symptoms and effects.

Early symptoms

For the first five days, people will typically only feel mild to moderate side effects like:

- Fever and chills
- Headache or muscle aches
- Fatigue
- Confusion
- Nausea, diarrhea, vomiting
- Loss of appetite
- Rash (less common)

Late-Stage Symptoms

If you are facing the later stages of this condition, you will typically have symptoms like:

- Respiratory distress
- Excessive, unexpected bleeding
- Septic shock
- Brain damage

Usually, people who have reached the point of having these symptoms will find little relief or any chance of a cure because the condition has already had such an impact on them. That is another reason why there is a push for better and faster reliable testing options. The goal is for people to get an accurate diagnosis of Lyme disease before they end up in the later stage symptoms and are unable to take back control of their condition.

Rocky Mountain Spotted Fever

Rocky Mountain Spotted Fever is caused by a bite from an infected American dog tick. It is also known as tick-borne typhus fever and is a condition with a host of symptoms and dangerous potential outcomes. It can also be spread by the Rocky Mountain wood tick and while cases can occur all over the U.S. and Mexico, they are most commonly found in Oklahoma, Arkansas, Tennessee, Missouri, and North Carolina.

This condition presents a lot of generic signs and symptoms, again making it hard to diagnose at first. Anyone who feels ill after being exposed to ticks or being in tick-borne areas should see a doctor immediately for the best chances of a full recovery from whatever tick-borne illness they've acquired.

Symptoms

Some of the common symptoms of Rocky Mountain Spotted Fever include:

- Fever
- Headache
- Rash
- Nausea and vomiting
- Muscle pain
- Stomach pain
- Loss of appetite

This condition is typically treated without incident. However, those who have severe RMSF may have permanent issues related to nerve damage, paralysis, mental disability, and other symptoms that were not addressed in time. Although this condition can be life-threatening, it can also be treated with antibiotics in adults and children, which makes early diagnosis an important factor for several reasons.

Ehrlichiosis

This condition is caused by the deer tick, and it is a general term more than an exact diagnosis. It refers to any diseases caused by the bacteria Ehrlichia chaffeensis, E. ewingii, or E. muris eauclairensis. This is a mild condition for most, which is treated with Doxycycline, an antibiotic that can alleviate all symptoms when taken early enough.

If treatment is delayed and antibiotics aren't taken within the first few weeks, late-stage symptoms can occur.

Symptoms

Common symptoms within the first five days of illness include:

- Fever and chills
- Muscle aches
- Headache
- Confusion
- Rashes (more likely in children)
- Nausea, vomiting, diarrhea
- Loss of appetite

Those who experience late-stage symptoms related to this condition will experience things like:

- Brain damage or nervous system damage
- Respiratory failure
- Uncontrolled bleeding
- Organ failure
- Death

Some risk factors make people more likely to experience late-stage symptoms, including age or having a weakened immune system. That's why it's important to see a doctor immediately if you have been bitten by a tick or experience any of the symptoms on the first list.

How to Safely and Effectively Remove a Tick

The sooner you remove a tick, the better. Not only will it be easier to get out when it hasn't had as much time to make itself at home, but it will reduce the risk of transmission of diseases like Lyme disease, Rocky Mountain Spotted Fever, and others discussed above.

There are several schools of thought and tips about the best ways to remove a tick. However, the basic process is the same, no matter where you look. Here's a step-by-step look at proper tick removal on humans and pets.

STEP ONE: GATHER TOOLS

If you're at home, get a pair of tweezers or a similar type of tool that can allow you to firmly grasp and grab the tick. If you don't get a good enough grip, their barbs may remain in your skin or you might not get the entire tick out. That's why having the right tools matters. If you are in a situation where you have to use your hands, protect them with gloves, tissue paper, or another barrier.

STEP TWO: PREPARE FOR REMOVAL

Removing the tick is the hardest part for a lot of people. You have to grasp it firmly and apply steady pressure. However, at the same time, you also have to make sure that you don't crush the tick or puncture its body, which can contain a variety of infectious bacteria and fluids. Using tweezers (or your fingers), practice gripping the tick firmly without smashing it until you feel confident that you can maintain a steady grasp.

STEP THREE: PULL THE TICK OUT

Now, you will want to grasp the tick with the tweezers or your fingers and pull very firmly and steadily upward and away from the skin. If the tick is in at an angle or in a position that's hard for you to reach, have someone assist you in the removal process. Once the tick has been removed, set it aside to save for further needs. Then, disinfect the area where the tick was and wash your hands with soap and water.

STEP FOUR: CHECK THE BITE SITE

Once the tick is gone, you might think you're out of the woods. However, depending on how much time the tick had before you pulled it out, you may already be infected with the bacteria that cause Lyme disease or other dangerous bacteria. Keep an eye on the bite site and make sure that you don't see a rash form (which usually looks like a bullseye) or that it doesn't start to swell or redden in any way. When in doubt, treatment should be taken.

STEP FIVE: CHECK EVERYWHERE (AND EVERYONE) ELSE

If there's one tick on you, there's a fair chance that there might be more. That's why a full inspection is a good idea. Inspect the rest of your body, your hairline, any crevices and dark areas (armpits, knee folds, behind the ears, etc.), and other places ticks might hide. Look around your ankles, too, or wherever your socks rest—ticks will take the easiest route to get on a host and then move from there to find the best hiding spot. Yours might not be hidden just yet.

Make sure that you know what ticks look like and how painfully small they can be. Here's a quick reference.

Pictured is the black-legged tick in its four lifecycles: larva, nymph, adult female, and adult male. As you can see, even the adult male isn't that big and could be hard to spot when they're carefully hidden and embedded in the skin.

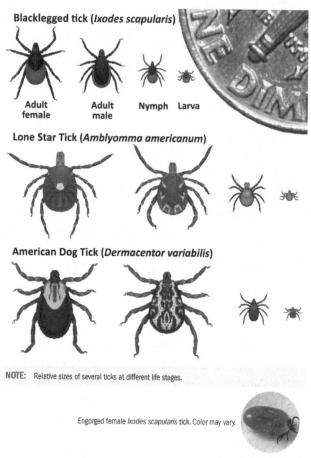

Blacklegged tick (*Ixodes scapularis*)

Adult female · Adult male · Nymph · Larva

Lone Star Tick (*Amblyomma americanum*)

American Dog Tick (*Dermacentor variabilis*)

NOTE: Relative sizes of several ticks at different life stages.

Engorged female *Ixodes scapularis* tick. Color may vary.

Get to know your ticks

Other ticks are similar in size but may have a different appearance, such as being a darker brown color. The younger the tick, the smaller it will be. You can be infected by a smaller, younger tick, so knowing all the sizes and stages is important.

What if I Didn't Get the Whole Tick?

If there is any question about the effectiveness of tick removal, you should contact a doctor immediately. I'm hopeful they will be able to help you determine whether or not the tick was properly removed. They will also have the tools to retrieve any left-behind barbs, legs, or other bits that may not have come out when you pulled the tick.

Even if you get most of a tick out, leaving any of it behind can still cause you to become infected with conditions like Lyme disease. And it's not just that—an ill-removed tick that isn't properly addressed could result in an infection or create other issues with your skin or your overall health.

What About Burning or Smothering Them?

Many on the east coast grew up the old wives' tales of burning a tick to encourage it to slide out. Others learned that petroleum jelly can suffocate these little pests and make their removal even easier. People often wonder if these methods are still used or if they were ever even effective to begin with. Here's the scoop.

Burning Ticks

Many people ascribe to the idea that using a lighter or match to burn an attached tick and encourage it to withdraw was an effective removal option. This was a "trick" used for years by many, but it's actually more harmful than good. Not only will it probably not work, but the sense of danger could cause the tick to release its guts into the bite preemptively, which makes it even more likely that people could wind up with Lyme disease or another tick-borne disease.

It's better to just use tweezers and approach the tick slowly. Apply slow, even pressure and pull the tick out carefully. That way, it won't be startled and it will be less likely to cause bigger issues for you as a result.

Petroleum Jelly (and Other Substances)

Suffocating the tick sounds like a good way to get it to detach, but that may not always be what happens. Plus, when you cover the tick in petroleum jelly, it becomes that much harder for you to get a good grip on it. That means you may struggle to get a full removal or cause more issues in the first place. And again, if it causes the tick to panic, you could end up in worse shape than where you began.

So, there you have it: everything you need to know about ticks, the diseases, their cause, and how to get rid of them. That's half the battle when it comes to the risk of conditions like Lyme disease. If you know how to properly respond to a tick embedding itself, you will be far more prepared to get it out quickly and safely.

CHAPTER 04

Research

Facts and Conclusions

A simple Internet search will reveal several sources of information regarding Lyme disease research. From the National Institutes of Health (NIH) to dedicated facilities like the Columbia University Lyme and Tick-Borne Disease Research Center and the Johns Hopkins Lyme Disease Research Center, ongoing efforts are being made to ensure that we learn as much as possible about Lyme disease and other tick-borne diseases. This will lead to future success in treatments and help prevent serious issues like neurological damage that happen as a result of a tick bite.

In 2020, the NIH invited those affected by Lyme disease to take part in studies to learn more about the condition. It included assistance with some travel costs for those who weren't local to the Bethesda, Maryland area, as they hoped to broaden their potential audience. The wider the audience, the more the NIH could learn about the disease.

Several other organizations and universities have conducted studies and research into Lyme disease, covering everything from how to identify ticks and tick bites to why the body's neurological system can be so affected by the condition in some, and not in others. Many of them also have research ongoing to learn more while also helping to better educate the medical community and the general public. Some of the biggest research groups and organizations include:

- Columbia University Irving Medical Center, Lyme, and Tick-Borne Diseases Research Center
- Johns Hopkins Lyme Disease Research Center
- Lyme Disease Working Group - Stanford Medicine
- Yale University
- Tufts University Lyme Disease Initiative
- The Lyme Disease Association, Inc. LymeDisease.org

Let's take a look at each of these organizations, including how long they've been around, what their mission is, and other details. Then, we'll dive into some of the latest and ongoing research from sources like the Washington Post, Science.org, and others. There are a lot of great efforts underway regarding the prevention and treatment of Lyme disease.

Research Organizations

As mentioned, this is not an exhaustive list of the organizations, universities, and others researching Lyme disease. However, it does cover the most well-known entities and provides a great launching point for learning more about all the ways that Lyme is being studied at this point.

Columbia University IMC Lyme and Tick-Borne Diseases Research Center

Columbia's Research Center was established in 2007. It was the product of a relationship between Columbia University, the Lyme Disease Association, Inc. (more on them later), and the Global Lyme Alliance. This became the first academic research facility in the U.S. to utilize multidisciplinary research to further investigate the chronic effects of Lyme disease and other tick-borne diseases. The mission of this organization involves: "Identifying better diagnostic assays, better treatments, and a better pathophysiologic understanding of the mechanisms of symptom persistence."

Their website includes tons of news and research, along with a section dedicated to patients who need to get more insight on treatment and other needs. They have also published a book and there is an e-newsletter that people can subscribe to if they want to stay updated on the research at Columbia.

Johns Hopkins Lyme Disease Research Center

The Johns Hopkins Lyme Disease Research Center is dedicated to patient-based research efforts, with a mission to address and understand the various manifestations of this disease and utilize their multidisciplinary research to deliver improved outcomes in patient care, health, and education.

The multidisciplinary research and clinical team at Johns Hopkins conducts a variety of groundbreaking research studies to help improve clinical and patient understanding of Lyme disease, as well as its manifestations, related diseases, etc. It posts news and updated information regularly, in addition to their studies and research publications.

Since 2015, the Johns Hopkins LDRC has seen more than 1,000 patients. It has office hours and allows people to schedule an appointment for study-related check-ups and treatments. It also has a mailing list with newsletters for Lyme disease, rheumatology, arthritis, lupus, myositis, scleroderma, and other conditions. There is a Lyme and Tickborne Disease Fellowship Program dedicated to helping train clinical and research physicians to help drive the advancement and understanding of this condition.

It's the first of its kind, and it offers rigorous, intensive fellowships that ensure that fellows get a full exposure to the world of Lyme disease, including what we know and what we have yet to understand. Candidates will need to have completed a residency program in family medicine, neurology, or internal medicine and will also have to provide documentation to prove their training and education.

The two-year program allows fellows to enter the growing field of Lyme disease research and treatment, practice evidence-based care, and even grow into leadership roles within healthcare facilities.

Stanford Medicine

Stanford Medicine is one of the programs on the list that doesn't have a dedicated Lyme disease focus, but it does have a collaborative clinical care, research, and education program that harnesses a research center and the health care delivery systems that they utilize. This allows it to make groundbreaking research insights and share relevant Lyme disease-related news in ways that some programs can't.

While Stanford isn't dedicated exclusively to Lyme disease, it does have a focus on infectious disease and that is where its experience and interest in Lyme comes into play. Stanford has a newsroom for adults and a special newsroom for children on the Stanford Medicine website, along with plenty of resources and information about the School of Medicine itself.

University of New Haven

The University of New Haven started research on Lyme disease with its own Lyme Disease Research Group in the early 2000s. The program has provided more than 90 graduate students with dedicated training and education in Lyme-related research, clinical elements, and other factors. One of the highlights is the program's identification of a worrisome increase in deer tick co-infection rates, including discovering some novel co-infections like microfilarial nematode and mycoplasma species.

Grants have been provided by a variety of organizations and foundations, including:

- Lyme Disease Association
- Lyme Research Alliance
- Turn the Corner Foundation
- California Lyme Disease Association
- Steven & Alexandra Cohen Foundation
- Bay Area Lyme Foundation

In addition, the school holds symposia regularly to encourage ongoing research and education into Lyme and other tick-borne illnesses. It studies different forms of the bacteria that cause Lyme disease, as well as how they work, to figure out why some people don't respond to antibiotics for Lyme and what can be done to provide better solutions moving forward.

Tufts University Lyme Disease Initiative

Tufts University has a Lyme Disease Initiative that is focused on developing research and has a very bold mission of eradicating Lyme disease by 2030. The researchers were awarded LymeX diagnostics funding to the tune of $1 million to help with their groundbreaking research, thanks to an application that was led by Dr. Peter Gwynn. The team is going to enter the second phase, focuses on clinical validations, and other research and studies will also continue.

This group is a combination of scientists and clinicians who are committed to working to find a cure and end to Lyme disease. They collaborate with researchers from other universities and organizations to explore new strategies for helping to eradicate Lyme as a human threat. The website has plenty of information about the group, Lyme disease, news and updates, and more.

The Lyme Disease Association, Inc.

This organization has been around for 31 years, offering tools and information to support research, education, patient support, and prevention efforts. The Lyme Disease Association began as an informal organization that was first registered as the Lyme Disease Association of New Jersey before expanding to become a national organization in the year 2000.

LDA-funded research has been seen in more than 60 publications, and it continues to work to find better solutions for prevention, treatment, and the increased understanding of Lyme disease. The website has information on doctors, government topics, grants, and even their LymeAid 4 Kids program, which was developed after a suggestion from Amy Tan, the acclaimed author who also had been a Lyme patient.

This program is designed to provide support for families and children who have Lyme disease or other tick-borne illnesses. These are families that often have no insurance or have financial difficulties related to using that insurance for Lyme treatment. Through the program, those under age 21 can receive as much as $1,000 towards the diagnosis and treatment of Lyme disease and related conditions.

Recent Lyme Disease Research

As mentioned, you don't have to look far to find research studies and news publications about Lyme disease, including in the current events section. This disease is still undergoing a lot of research and scrutiny with the hopes that we can better understand it and then use that understanding to create better treatments, cures, and preventive options.

NIAID (National Institute of Allergy and Infectious Diseases) Research

The NIAID is specifically focused on diagnostics research related to Lyme disease. It has recognized the need for rapid, point-of-care testing solutions to diagnose this condition and its doing its part by supporting various research efforts. The goals include finding new substances that diagnostic tools might be able to measure to improve the sensitivity and specificity of testing to deliver better accuracy in test results.

Because Lyme is currently so difficult to diagnose, it leaves plenty of room for gaining more information and insight. Even the characteristic "bullseye" rash doesn't occur in as many as 25 percent of those who are infected with Lyme disease. And while current Lyme antibody tests are useful to identify antibodies in the blood, it can take a few weeks of fighting the condition before these antibodies appear. This means that diagnosis takes longer, leaving more room for the disease to cause damage.

The NIAID supports a host of research projects related to Lyme disease and its diagnosis. Because there are so many different tests available, it can be nearly impossible to address accuracy with all the existing options. This is why the NIAID focuses on research that highlights new diagnostic testing solutions with more accurate results that can be obtained sooner.

Some of the examples of projects that NIAID is supporting include those looking at T-cell measurements, using metabolomics to identify infection biomarkers, and novel antigens that can be measured for more effective treatment.

APA Research - Lyme Disease and Its Impact on Mental Health

In June 2022, the APA published an article discussing the mental health effects of conditions like Lyme and tick-borne diseases. It is widely known that undiagnosed or untreated Lyme disease can lead to chronic mental health symptoms. Even when treated, people may still experience problems with fatigue, concentration, focus, anxiety and depression, and more.

The APA points out that many people who suffer from Lyme are dealing with a poor quality of life and debilitating symptoms that can make it hard to function. This can lead to several mental health issues and cause a lot of stress for people.

Research has also shown that the disease itself can directly cause its own mental health concerns. In a recent study, those who were diagnosed as having Lyme disease in a hospital setting were 28 percent more likely to suffer from mental health disorders. Not only that, but they were twice as likely to have a suicide attempt than those without a Lyme diagnosis.

The Need for Tailored Therapeutic Approaches

Upon initial diagnosis, patients may need a wealth of information about Lyme and tick-borne diseases, along with validation of their condition and experience. In one example, a teen was being treated for an infection that came from a tick while simultaneously experiencing intrusive thoughts. This had never been a problem in the past, but with reassurance that the brain plays tricks on Lyme patients, she was able to cope better.

Patients have a lot of frustration, demoralization, and other issues that appear when they are also diagnosed with Lyme disease. Largely because of the lack of available information and help, those who are diagnosed feel isolated and aren't sure where to turn for help.

This also leads to an increased need for better awareness of Lyme, its symptoms and potential outcomes, and the best ways to treat and prevent the condition. Those who are already affected will want to have a custom treatment plan developed that includes the appropriate mental health therapies and services to ensure that the disease doesn't have more of a debilitating effect than necessary.

The bottom line? For providers, taking care of patients who have Lyme disease requires flexible thinking, an open mind, and a willingness to take a creative approach to therapy and treatment to provide the best outcomes. The population is a challenging one to work with, but it's also one that is rewarding for those who do it and do it well.

Further research is ongoing to get a better idea of how mental health issues and Lyme disease affect each other and coexist in the body, which means there may be hope for an even better solution in the future.

Biomarker Research (2022)

2022 turned out to be a banner year for discoveries on how genetic analysis of patients might reveal unique biomarkers or genetic 'fingerprints' that could be used to better diagnose those suffering from various stages of Lyme disease. In July 2022 Charles Chiu, M.D., Ph.D. (Department of Laboratory Medicine, University of California, San Francisco, CA), in collaboration with John Aucott, M.D. (Lyme Disease Research Center, Johns Hopkins School of Medicine, Baltimore, MD), reported that profiling 31 distinct genes could discriminate between early Lyme patients and healthy controls. Perhaps most importantly, this diagnostic strategy yielded an overall sensitivity of 90.0%, specificity of 100%, and accuracy of 95.2%. These results highlight the potential clinical utility of a gene expression approach for diagnosis of early Lyme disease, including in patients negative by conventional CDC two-tiered antibody testing.

Then in November, Cell Reports Medicine published an article about the ongoing research related to biomarkers to differentially diagnose Lyme disease. This study set out to identify and focus on a set of genes specifically activated only in those with long-term Lyme disease. As many as 20% of the people affected by this condition suffer from long-term and chronic symptoms.

The study involved 152 patients that had post-treatment Lyme disease. The patient had been treated with a two to four week course of oral antibiotics, but continues to have symptoms of pain, fatigue, or difficulty thinking that lasts for more than 6 months after they finish treatment. Scientists sequenced RNA from each of these patients and then compared that data with the RNA sequencing of 72 patients that were diagnosed with acute Lyme disease. They also had 44 control subjects in the study with no Lyme disease present.

Their results showed that there were definite changes in

the gene expression of those who have acute or chronic Lyme disease. Not only that, but the changes in expression were unique to each condition. They compared this to other infectious diseases and their gene expression profiles and then used AI and machine learning to narrow things down more.

The result is that they have identified 35 unique biomarkers that can help distinguish those with both types of Lyme disease from those who aren't afflicted. The plan is to use this information to develop better diagnostic tests for future needs. A genetic test would be an improvement when compared to existing testing methods, which rely largely on antibodies.

Current testing methods take a lot of time and can be unreliable based on things like exposure, immune activity, and other factors. With these recent advances in genetic testing, scientists and healthcare professionals could easily identify the biomarkers present (or not present) to determine whether someone has Lyme disease, as well as whether it is acute or chronic.

Although this is a big discovery, it's just the beginning of what's to come for genetics and genetic testing for Lyme disease. This will surely revolutionize the way that Lyme is diagnosed and treated, and perhaps offer more accuracy to reduce the risk of chronic and lifelong debilitating symptoms related to Lyme. Such improvements in diagnosis can move the Lyme disease field in the direction of personalized medicine, which has been so successful in improving the diagnosis and treatment of cancer patients.

This is Just the Start

That's probably a lot of research to cover in a short space, but it shows a lot of promise. Lyme disease might be a condition that is currently limited in resources and information, but that won't last forever. There are a growing number of organizations and universities that are studying this condition and how to better treat it from all angles, including coexisting mental health issues and more.

If this is what current research has done, imagine what's to come. As more precise methods for diagnosis and testing of Lyme disease are created and approved, fewer people will have to live with the condition or worry about whether they will find the right treatment. Antibiotics have their place, but there's so much more potential with this disease, so long as we keep learning.

CHAPTER 05

Testing

Not All are Created Equal

Testing for Lyme disease is limited and often frustrating, to say the least. Early detection is difficult because there is often a lack of immediate symptoms, aside from the tick bite that may or may not have been discovered yet. It's important to save the tick after you remove it so it can be tested.

As mentioned earlier, the testing options for this condition are limited and sometimes they create false outcomes because they aren't perfected. The National Institute of Health (NIH) published a piece on Lyme disease diagnostics research that sums up the majority of the concerns and considerations and points out that there is a growing need for the development of point-of-care tests that can rapidly determine whether people have been infected with Lyme disease.

Within the NIH, the National Institute of Allergy and Infectious Diseases handles the diagnostics and other areas of research specifically related to Lyme disease. Their priorities are to find targets, including substances that tools can measure from patient samples, as well as to improve the sensitivity and accuracy of the tests that are currently available.

Read on to learn more about obstacles and considerations, current approaches, and what the research for the future looks like. Although we still have a lot to learn about Lyme disease, there's also been a lot that's been done since it first showed up in the United States, and the research is ongoing.

Considerations and Obstacles

Lyme disease is difficult to diagnose in some instances. For starters, many of the common symptoms are also common for countless other conditions and diseases. Plus, the trademark bullseye rash doesn't even appear in about 25% of those who are infected with this disease. Current diagnostic testing methods aren't always capable of early detection because antibodies take time to reach detectable levels.

Treatment is much more effective in the early stages of Lyme disease. Therefore, if doctors are unable to make an early diagnosis, people are less likely to find a treatment that will fully eliminate the Lyme bacteria or treat them without any lingering effects. Doctors also need to know whether a patient is actively infected or if they were exposed at an earlier time in their life.

The limitations of current tests make getting a clear, quick diagnosis a challenge. Although there are several things a doctor will go over in trying to determine a Lyme disease diagnosis, Lyme antibody tests are the most popular and reliable. The problem, as mentioned, is that these tests take time because it can take weeks for an antibody response to develop. In the meantime, the Lyme bacteria is free to travel around the body through the bloodstream and invade different organs such as the joints, heart, and central (brain) and peripheral nervous systems.

In addition to the potential for false negative results, you can also have false positive results. While a false negative result can be caused by poor sensitivity of the test or looking for antibodies before they are produced, false positive results can occur if a diagnostic test is not sufficiently specific for Lyme disease or a person's immune system stops producing antibodies against the Lyme bacteria.

These are just a couple of the big obstacles that highlight the growing need for improved diagnostic tools and testing methods that can help provide earlier diagnosis and treatment.

Current Diagnostic Approaches

Currently, healthcare providers will use approved laboratory tests combined with a discussion regarding the symptoms a patient is experiencing to diagnose Lyme disease. The CDC advises that a standard two-tiered testing process be used to ensure that a patient has Lyme disease. As mentioned above, most current testing for Lyme disease only checks for antibodies, not the actual bacteria. So, these assays could create false negative or false positive results or identify antibodies from a past infection, which means the patient may not be actively infected but had prior, resolved infection.

CDC-Recommended Two-Step Testing

Both tiers detect antibodies against the Lyme bacteria. The first and second tier tests serve two very important and distinct purposes. The first tier is very sensitive but not specific whereas the second tier is not very sensitive but it is very specific. This is why the second test should not be used on its own but only after a positive or equivocal test result is returned by the first-tier assay. Relying on a first-tier test only could result in false negative results or false positive results due to lack of specificity. Both scenarios are to be avoided because true Lyme patients may suffer from delayed treatment and patients that do not have Lyme disease may be treated for a bacterial infection they do not have – again, delaying appropriate treatment for what does ails them.

Finally, a test result should not be used to diagnose Lyme disease in the absence of a clinical case history consistent with a clinical diagnosis of Lyme disease. The reverse is also true, a clinical diagnosis of Lyme disease and a negative test result could result in the misdiagnosis of a patient suffering from a disease that mimics Lyme disease. Such Lyme mimics include multiple sclerosis, ALS, chronic fatigue syndrome, and Long Haul COVID-19, to name a few.

ELISA Testing

ELISA testing isn't just for Lyme disease. Doctors who suspect that their patients may be suffering from any number of diseases may find that they could benefit from this testing. ELISA stands for Enzyme-Linked Immunosorbent Assay, which is a fancy way of saying that the test utilizes a pathogen's protein antigens as 'bait' to capture specific antibodies (the "fish") raised against these foreign microbial proteins.

Antibodies show that the body is trying to fight off disease. The detection of antigen-capture of specific antibodies is indicated by a color reaction that occurs as part of the ELISA. A color change indicates the presence of antibodies to a particular microbe and under certain circumstances the absence of color indicates your immune system has never seen the microbe before.

ELISAes can also determine the severity or stage of the condition being tested for, but that depends on the exact protein antigens being used. While older ELISA tests could take days to weeks to return a result to doctors, more recently developed assays can return results within minutes to hours. This significantly reduces the time between when you visit the doctor and when they may decide the best approach to treating you. Importantly, the sooner an accurate diagnosis is made and appropriate treatment is started the better the prognosis for a complete or near complete recovery from Lyme disease and other tick-borne diseases.

Lyme Western Blot Test

The Lyme Western Blot test is another type of antibody test that is used to determine whether someone has Lyme disease. It is more specific than the ELISA test, which makes it a great secondary test to either confirm or deny the existence of Lyme. Some people try to use it as a first-time confirmation test because it can get a good result even within a week of exposure. Patients will continue to test positive until the bacteria have been completely removed from the body.

Blood is taken and certain enzymes are connected with the antibodies in your bloodstream. This allows them to test and see how high your antibodies are and if that could be a result of Lyme disease.

IGeneX

IGeneX is a brand of testing products that makes Lyme Western Blot testing kits that you can purchase for use at home. This is an antibody-based test that will indicate whether your immune system has been exposed to B. burgdorferi, the bacteria known to cause Lyme disease. This specific test brand focuses on delivering a host of tests for different conditions, including antibody tests for a host of different conditions and diseases.

You can select from a host of products when you choose to work with IGeneX, including a Multiplex PCR Lyme test that checks your serum levels and other aspects of your blood to ensure that you are always in the best health.

Sofia® 2 Lyme FIA test

The Sofia® 2 Lyme FIA test is designed to provide rapid testing results with more accuracy than other tests on the market. Using immunofluorescence-based lateral-flow technology, the differential detection of antibodies is identified and classified to arrive at a diagnosis. FIA stands for Fluorescent Immunoassay, which is the method used to recognize the presence of Lyme bacteria-specific anti-bodies without relying on a color reaction.

Results are available in three to 15 minutes, and the test is simple and easy to perform. It can get results from a finger stick instead of a full blood draw, making it less invasive and demanding than other tests on the market today. Plus, it provides results for IgM and IgG in the same test and results are quick enough that anyone can get ahead of their Lyme disease diagnosis.

These tests are currently only used by select healthcare providers, but they are gaining popularity as more desirable testing methods are needed to complement if not replace the old CDC standard two-tiered assay. The benefits are many, but the fact that you can get more accurate, faster results is reason enough to have this particular test performed if you think that you have Lyme disease.

The speed of testing and the lack of need for a serious blood draw allows people to use this test at point-of-care facilities such as a doctor's office or local pharmacy. Eventually, highly accurate (sensitive and specific) tests may be available for use at home, like COVID-19 rapid antigen test kits. However, it may be more cost-effective to visit a doctor to have them do the testing, for the sake of insurance and other matters. Not only that, but doctors will know what to look for and how to read the test results most effectively.

LIAISON LymeDetect®

This test is designed to offer more accuracy by combining IgG and IgM assays with patented technology to ensure that patients get a reliable, effective diagnosis within weeks so that there is less risk of things getting to a more severe place. This new test is focused on providing better patient outcomes and more economic benefits to the healthcare system. Early detection through a combination of approaches is what sets this test apart.

LIAISON has demonstrated an improvement in testing results, including in sensitivity and early detection. This can reduce the incidence of untreated infections that can lead to more serious complications. Plus, the testing has an automated, traceable workflow that allows it to fit seamlessly into existing lab routines. It eliminates hands-on and subjective test reading and reduces the risk of human error. The closed-loop automated test delivers clear, reliable results.

You can get an accurate diagnosis in 24 hours or less with this test, which is highly reliable and designed to help limit the serious effects of untreated Lyme disease and other conditions.

Accuracy vs. Affordability of Testing

The biggest issue in the diagnosis and treatment of Lyme disease is a serious lack of accurate testing options. So far, most of the tests out there focus on identifying the anti-bodies that fight Lyme instead of looking for indications of the disease itself. Until that changes, it is unlikely that tests will become any more accurate.

When you're only testing for antibodies, it's going to be easy to get false negatives and positives or only get partial information. That can make it increasingly difficult to get an early diagnosis and with a condition like Lyme disease, that can be a critical error. As seen earlier in the book, those who get diagnosed and treated while their symptoms are still in the early stages will have a much better chance of full recovery than those who don't get treatment until they have reached the late stages of Lyme disease.

Most of the testing options are also quite expensive. For example, to buy the IGeneX testing kit, you'll have to spend $125 out of pocket. However, these tests are also covered by insurance for most of the people who have it, so that's an important factor to consider.

More Testing Options to Come

Part of the future of Lyme disease research is going to be in developing better testing options and more efficient test solutions that get accurate results. This is going to take some time, of course, but it won't be long before there are even more competitors in the market that offer solutions for Lyme testing that are more effective and accurate than ever before.

Home tests, finger-prick tests instead of blood draws, and access to affordable testing options are the highlights of the current medical field concerning Lyme disease. As much as people talk about how limited the current testing options are, the future remains bright. Research is being planned by companies all over the country and the world to learn more about Lyme disease and how to use testing to get a more accurate diagnosis.

As we learn more about the condition and how to properly identify it, that will impact the types of tests available, too. If you need Lyme testing or other diagnostic testing for antibodies, you should talk to your doctor about the options that are out there so that you can get an accurate diagnosis that allows you to move forward with your life.

CHAPTER 06

Treatment

Traditional and Complementary

With testing and diagnosis comes the need for treatment. Anyone who has been diagnosed with Lyme disease will need to know what they should do to keep the infection at bay and potentially eradicate the bacteria to get their life back. Typically, antibiotics are chosen to treat Lyme disease, offering a more rapid recovery for those who are earlier in the condition. Generally, recovery will be better for those who get a quicker diagnosis.

Usually, antibiotic treatment will last for 10 to 14 days, depending on the symptoms presenting and how severe the condition is. Treatment may take longer if you have a more serious case of Lyme disease or if it was diagnosed late. Those who get a later diagnosis or who are more seriously affected by the disease could be given IV antibiotics for up to six months to get faster results.

IV antibiotics can also assist with the alleviation of arthritis, and related symptoms, conditions affecting the heart, and conditions affecting the nervous system in relation to how they are exacerbated by Lyme disease. If you aren't sure which course of treatment is best, do your research, come prepared and talk to your doctor.

Preventive Antibiotics

Some medical professionals will prescribe antibiotics as a preventive measure. If someone has been in an area where Lyme disease is common or where ticks are more prevalent, and they were bitten by a deer tick that was in their skin for more than 36 hours, then they can be put on antibiotics proactively. This can help alleviate the symptoms or get rid of the condition before it even has a chance to become a serious issue.

Remember, however, that the three criteria above all need to be met for a doctor to choose this route and we know this is not always the case. If you only meet one or two, your doctor might want to wait or do further testing to make sure that nothing else is wrong.

Related Conditions and Treatments

Letting Lyme go untreated can result in Chronic Lyme disease, suffering from a range of life altering conditions, arthritic-type symptoms and even difficulty thinking and handling neurological tasks. There are four main areas of focus, including the trademark rash of Lyme disease and the various conditions that affect the body:

Erythema migrans: This is the rash that is typically seen as one of the first signs of Lyme disease. It is also known as the bullseye rash but can appear differently on everyone.

Neurologic Lyme disease: This is a condition usually caused by undiagnosed and untreated Lyme. The disease affects the nervous system, causing issues with weakness, paralysis, decreased memory and concentration, sleep issues, and more.

Lyme carditis: Lyme carditis refers to a condition where Lyme bacteria enter the heart tissues. This can affect the healthy electrical operation of your heart and can cause serious issues for those with existing heart concerns.

Lyme arthritis: When Lyme bacteria invade the joints and cause inflammation, swelling, and joint pain, this is known as Lyme arthritis. The sooner it is treated, the less likely the effects will be permanent.

There is an increasing need for additional research that can assist in providing a better understanding of how to treat, manage, and support those who have symptoms of Chronic Lyme disease. Below are a handful of treatment options all provided to inspire you to research and question what may work for you.

Approved Lyme Disease Treatment Options

Currently, the only approved treatment for Lyme disease as we know involves the use of antibiotics. Usually, a short course of oral antibiotics, such as amoxicillin or doxycycline, is enough to treat the condition for most people. This depends on it being treated early, however, as late-stage conditions may require more aggressive treatment. Some Lyme patients may see better results with extended antibiotic therapy, which usually lasts between three and four weeks of oral antibiotics and up to six months of IV antibiotics.

There are a number of serious reasons why prolonged antibiotic use is not good for our body. One simply being the importance of our microbiome (gut) being the majority of our immune system and mental regulation. Additional long-term exposure of antibiotics can cause the bacteria in the body to build up a tolerance and be able to continue wreaking havoc. Some doctors hesitate to prescribe long term oral antibiotics too frequently for this reason, and in the case of Lyme disease, it can present an ongoing concern.

Doctors are also learning the various ways these treatments can be spaced out and manipulated to produce better results. Patients who have more severe symptoms may be given stronger antibiotics from the start to ensure they attack the bacteria more aggressively. Chronic Lyme patients who try a more aggressive treatment plan can experience a Herx reaction causing their symptoms to be worse. The Herx reaction is basically a die-off of the bacteria. Patients have responded to Herx so poorly, they need to stop or postpone treatment. Again, this is why it's important to get a good doctor and openly communicate with them your symptoms and reactions. They should look at your specific case more holistically and help you get the right treatment, no matter what that might be.

In the future, the FDA may approve other therapies and treatments to assist with Lyme, but that remains to be seen. In this chapter, we will cover a host of alternative and complementary therapies that are being studied and used to help alleviate the symptoms of Lyme and related conditions. While these have been and are being researched, they have already shown some promise.

The Cost of Lyme Disease Treatment

Antibiotic treatment is relatively affordable, and many people may even be able to get their insurance company to cover the cost or part of the antibiotics and other treatments. This could involve your doctor talking to the insurance company or submitting a claim the old-fashioned way, but it also never hurts to call and ask what kind of coverage you have.

Most of the complementary therapies discussed in the next section probably won't be covered by your insurance. However, it is always worth asking since I know insurance covers alternative therapies like acupuncture for pain. The best thing that you can do is check your insurance policy and see what kind of coverage you have. Never hurts to ask.

Of course, the real cost here is when people don't get the treatment they need—many suffer from chronic pain and other symptoms that can lead to a lifetime of distress, discomfort, and illness. If you think you have been bitten by an infected tick, don't hesitate to visit a doctor immediately. Otherwise, you could risk joining the rising number of people who go without early diagnosis and suffer in silence.

Alternative and Complementary Treatments for Lyme Disease

Many people seek out information on complementary and alternative treatment options for Lyme disease. However, while these methods and treatments are plentiful, it's important I note that they are not approved by the FDA or any other regulatory authority, and therefore should be used wisely.

Holistic and alternative modalities for healing are flooding our global society and I personally love to see it. We are going back to the hold ways of healing and becoming more proactive about preventative care. In this section we will mainly talk about alternative treatments related to Lyme. Alternative treatments range from supplementation to energy medicine.

Below is a very high-level look at the various treatment options Lyme patients have been experimenting with and seeing results. Keep in mind alternative therapies are more powerful when complimenting other therapies. For example, when you detox your body, you must rebuild and restore. When taking high doses of antibiotics you should also be rebuilding the gut with probiotics.

Supplements are a very easy and accessible treatment option, Lyme patients experiencing immune deficiency. Some supplements can help support by boosting the body's immune system, such as:

- B vitamins
- Vitamin C
- Fish oil
- Garlic
- Turmeric
- Alpha lipoic acid
- Magnesium

In addition to supplements, many people consider alternative therapies like:

- Hyperbaric oxygen therapy
- Infrared Sauna
- Chelation therapy

- Ultraviolet therapy
- Ozone therapy
- Energy medicine
- Bee venom
- Ketamine
- Stem Cells
- And more..

Again, these are not approved but patients have reported relief from treatment. It truly is just a matter of trying different remedies and finding what works.

For those who are working with a medical provider, it will be important to discuss the various therapies and treatment options available. You can also compare the different options to the state of your condition and the level of its severity. Most doctors and healthcare professionals will be on board to help you find the best relief, even if there's nothing that antibiotics or medical treatment can do.

Throughout the rest of this chapter, we'll take a closer look at some of the most popular therapeutic solutions for Lyme disease, including how they work, what kind of success rates they have.

Ozone Therapy

High-dose ozone therapy has proven to assist in the killing of bacteria, viruses, and fungi related to Lyme disease. That leads to the alleviation of serious joint pain and other Lyme symptoms. It helps rejuvenate healthy cells while killing off infected cells using an alternative form of oxygen that is known as ozone.

This advanced treatment can add ozone to as much as 2

liters of blood, which does more than standard ozone therapy. Those considering the treatment should make sure
that they choose high-dose services for the best results. By
increasing the amount of oxygen in the body, the patient
is helping their body fight off several potential effects and
conditions.

In addition to support for Lyme disease, this therapy is
often utilized to assist with:

- Diabetes
- Immune disorders
- Breathing disorders

Essentially, anyone who is trying to fight off infection or
bacteria could benefit from this therapy. However, some
medical professionals argue that it is ineffective at best—
done in the right circumstances, and with proper medical
support, it probably won't hurt to try. You'll want to discuss
this and other alternative therapies with your provider if
you are considering them.

Rife Machines

Different sources put the likelihood of health improvement
between 30 and 40 percent with Rife machine therapy. Rife
developed special microscopes to see germs and a unique
electromagnetic machine to kill those germs. Put simply,
the bacteria have a frequency and the machine would
send a higher frequency to kill them. Although it was quite
effective, his claims of being able to see and kill germs
with these tools have not been scientifically validated by
other experts.

Nonetheless, Rife machines are made by a variety of companies and are popular in Lyme forums. There is little to no harm utilizing a Rife machine, but it has been reported that Lyme patients can Herx.

If someone is struggling to find support and treatment for their Lyme disease, this option should be one that you explore. It could have some benefit, and there's no risk involved since it's all done electromagnetically.

FMT

Also known as a fecal microbiota transplant, this treatment option is used for several instances of IBS, C.diff and obesity, along with a few other conditions. This treatment is usually best after antibiotics have been taken to fight the bacteria. The concept of this treatment is simple. A "donor" will provide a healthy fecal sample, which will be transplanted into the affected person. The idea is that this will replace their gut microbiome, which is often destroyed from Lyme and antibiotics treatments.

When the gut microbiome and the body's natural bacteria aren't doing what they are supposed to do, it can have several different effects. This may seem like a radical treatment to some, but for those who have used it for IBS and other conditions, it has proven to be quite successful. This is a complementary therapy that isn't FDA-approved for Lyme disease. For many, it offers tons of gut health support and immune support, which is why it remains popular and continues to be studied for future uses.

Ivermectin

Tick bites introduce bacteria into the body, which is what leads to the development of Lyme disease. Along with that, it's been proposed that some parasites can also be associated with the development of Lyme disease. Instead of standard antibiotic therapy, or in addition to it, some doctors have been investigating the effectiveness of a drug known as Ivermectin.

Known as an antihelminth drug, this drug has been used for a long time in the treatment of parasites and is often prescribed by veterinarians to handle parasite infections in cats and dogs. Why is this important?

For starters, research is positing the question of whether Lyme disease patients can also be co-infected with filarial nematode, a species of parasite that infects more than 120 million people around the world. Many use mosquitos as their vector, but the possibility that ticks are now a vector as well is up for debate. The identification of this relationship can lead to future developments in testing and treatment for Lyme disease.

Patients with tick bite history could offer a target group for future research and the exploration of how to better address chronic Lyme disease symptoms and related conditions. This research is new and ongoing, but it shows a lot of promise.

Hyperbaric Oxygen Therapy

The body thrives on oxygen, so it makes sense that therapies like hyperbaric oxygen therapy have become so popular. Plus, they don't just treat one disease. Several conditions can be considered for treatment with this option, depending both on the condition itself and the symptoms that are present. Much like with ozone therapy, the idea is to saturate the blood with oxygen, which is believed to help kill the viruses and bacteria in the body's cells.

The increased blood flow and oxygen in the blood are exactly what Lyme disease doesn't want—the condition thrives in a low-oxygen environment. There are no guarantees or proven results with this therapy, but it does offer a lot of potential hope. Plus, research is ongoing into the use of this therapy to support immune health in other ways, thanks to its ability to enhance the defenses of the body's white blood cells.

Ketamine

Most people know ketamine as a drug that is used for treating some mental health conditions and offering additional health support. While it can be dangerous when used illegally and recreationally, ketamine is quite helpful to the body in the right forms and doses. This is why there is a growing number of ketamine therapy providers and services around the country.

Ketamine therapy for Lyme disease is focused on alleviating the chronic pain that comes with the condition. Ongoing arthritic and joint pain, along with other discomfort and pain related to this disease, are addressed by doctors to determine an effective therapy process.

Each patient will have a consultation that will help discover their health concerns, what they're hoping to get from ketamine therapy, and information on how ketamine works, potential side effects and risks, etc. Once the patient has the information, they will be able to decide whether this is a viable treatment option. This treatment is done through an IV and is closely monitored by medical professionals. It has shown great promises with those suffering from mental health issues such as depression and severe anxiety as well.

Stem Cells

Stem cell therapy has come into the spotlight lately as a viable treatment option for Lyme disease. Mesenchymal stem cells are known to have strong anti-inflammatory and immunomodulatory effects. This means that stem cells can alter the body's immune system while also reducing inflammation. That leads to relief from some of the most serious symptoms of Lyme disease. While it isn't a cure, per se, it is definitely going to give a lot of people hope.

Stem cell therapy is done through IV treatments and is used for several different conditions and illnesses:

- Spinal cord injuries
- Parkinson's disease
- ALS
- Burns
- Cancer
- Heart disease
- Diabetes
- Autoimmune diseases
- Neurological and traumatic injuries

Stem cells are usually employed later in the disease, as they can usually be cured with simple antibiotics when it is caught early and treated right away. Studies are being done on the use of MSC (mesenchymal stem cells) to assist with Post-Treatment Lyme Disease Syndrome.

PTLDS refers to a condition where the body faces prolonged exposure to Lyme disease and all of its various symptoms, which can lead to a host of other problems, including low immune function and excessive inflammation, pain, and chronic neurological issues. The addition of stem cells allows the body to get a healthy boost so that it can fight Lyme and other degenerative conditions while providing immune support for the body.

Stem cell therapy is an alternative option for Lyme disease and may not produce results in some patients.

Bee Venom

Bee venom therapy, or BVT for short, is a relatively new therapy that people are trying to assist with Lyme disease symptoms and relief. The approach has been studied by the University of New Haven's Lyme Disease Research Group and has shown that some people could find relief from Lyme symptoms with the assistance of bee venom. This, of course, must be obtained from the source, so those considering it must be prepared to get stung.

Those who are allergic to bees or other stinging insects, of course, should proceed with caution or avoid this treatment option. There is also more research that needs to be done to discover how this process works, as well as a better way for people to get the venom from the bees in the first place. Currently, this process is non-sustainable for treatment or the environment.

PK Protocol

The PK Protocol was first practiced in Europe but was soon brought to the U.S. to assist with neurological conditions like ALS, Alzheimer's Autism, Epilepsy, MS, Parkinson's, Lyme disease, and more. There are three parts to this process, which is only practiced by certain professionals who understand all of the elements of it. The protocol was developed by Dr. Patricia Kane, hence the "PK" in the name.

The PK Protocol involves three steps or parts:

- IV infusions
- Organic paleo/keto diet
- Oral supplements

To get started, anyone using this method will take a blood test that includes several different panels. The test gets sent back to BodyBio lab, which is owned by Dr. Kane, and then your doctor and Dr. Kane will consult on the results to create a custom treatment plan for each patient. This will help identify different risks, the body's current state of health, etc.

The second step is the IV infusions. These are usually a mixture of phosphatidylcholine and various vitamins, including B12. The infusions are designed to help the cells heal and to provide the body with the energy that it needs to fight Lyme and other conditions. In addition to this, a customized supplement plan will be created based on the results of the blood chemistry testing. This ensures that you get the correct supplementation strategy, no matter what your body needs.

This process is a slow one, but some people have seen results after sticking with it for some time. The goal is to help the body's cells heal, which will not only help get rid of the harmful effects of Lyme but potentially eliminate the condition and its effects.

Azlocillin

Azlocillin is a relatively new choice for Lyme treatment. Several antibiotics and similar medications have been tested over the years for effectiveness in alleviating Lyme symptoms and bacteria. Some are more effective than others and recently, Azlocillin has come to light as a possible treatment against Lyme that can address lingering symptoms and long-term effects.

It can kill the bacteria completely from the onset, which can do a lot to save people from arriving at late-stage symptoms and having to deal with the more dangerous effects of Lyme. Recent studies have shown that this medication beats out thousands of other compounds because its effectiveness in killing the bacteria was much higher.

This drug is not on the market yet, but it has been tested in mouse models and lab dishes, and more is on the horizon. An oral form of the drug will be used to conduct human clinical trials. As it stands, this may be a new option for those who don't respond to other antibiotics when treating Lyme disease.

IVIG

Intravenous immunoglobulin, or IVIG, is a therapy that has been used to treat Lyme disease and several of the complications that come from having the condition in the first place. This therapy is effective because it pulls antibodies from donor plasma and then gives them to the person affected through IV, allowing them to help build a stronger immune system.

When people are afflicted with Lyme disease, they face any number of complications and potential health issues. The body's defenses are down and the antibodies are working overtime, which may require the need for reinforcements. This therapy does just that, boosting the overall immune system and providing relief from chronic and ongoing symptoms of Lyme.

IVIG is also used to treat several other conditions that rely on healthy plasma and antibodies. Currently, it has been approved by the FDA for the treatment of six different conditions:

- Immune thrombocytopenic purpura (ITP)
- Primary and secondary immunodeficiency
- Pediatric HIV
- Kawasaki disease
- Graft versus host disease (GVHD)
- Bone marrow transplant infections

IVIG is most commonly used to treat chronic neuropathy and related conditions, including chronic inflammation. While this therapy isn't approved for use in Lyme patients specifically, that's only due to a lack of research and available proof of efficacy. It's likely that with time and research, the FDA will add this and other complementary treatments to the list of approved options for Lyme disease.

Find the Right Treatment for Your Lyme Diagnosis

These are just a handful of the options for Lyme disease therapy and alternative treatments. As you can see, although there is a lot of progress being made, many of the studies are still pending results, and there isn't a lot of cut-and-dry information when it comes to solving the Lyme disease dilemma. Anyone with this condition that continues to have symptoms after initial antibiotic treatment may need to consider these options.

The best thing that you can do is talk to your doctor and make sure that you understand the different treatment options and how best to address your specific condition.

Lyme disease can be scary because there is so much limited information, but there is plenty of hope, as you can see. And just because treatments and therapies aren't FDA-approved (yet), they do offer hope.

Those who have late-stage or chronic Lyme disease and its related symptoms will find the most relief from alternative and complementary options. However, you'll also want to remember that the results will vary for everyone, and what works for someone else might not work best for you.

You can see this reality further reflected in the collection of Lyme disease stories.

Part Two

Stories

BEFORE WE BEGIN

We've covered a lot of information, but it's still just a fraction of what could be known about Lyme disease. The Lyme community needs more access to funding and research, we would see significant progress. We need to improve awareness in the global population as well as the medical community, leading to an educated conversation around Lyme disease. Yet for most people, what ties it all together is hearing the stories of those who have been affected by Lyme disease and knowing you are not alone.

I'm talking about those who have struggled to find an answer for their mysterious symptoms; those who have been thought "crazy" by the medical professional when tests come back negative; and those who have gone through doctor after doctor after doctor, for years only to find out they have a condition that also doesn't have much in the way of treatment options.

The Lyme community is not as small as you think. Their stories can give us all inspiration- and help us find a path forward, together.

Note: The answers to the questions below are paraphrased from each interviewee's direct responses and edited for brevity and clarity which has been done with their full consent.

Dear WARRIOR,

Do Not
Settle for
Less.

YOU
Deserve More.

HANNAH OLSON

Massachusetts, USA

Resilient

Capable

Ambitious

Hannah Olson, co-founder of Chronically Capable, is our first interview. I had the pleasure of speaking with Hannah and learning about her struggles with Lyme, including her difficult road to diagnosis and the treatment that followed.

Where did your journey begin?

It's interesting, actually, because I grew up in the Cape Cod area of Massachusetts, so ticks were always around. I would spend hours playing outside, running through the woods, and then coming home at the end of the day to regular self-checks for ticks. And I never had an issue, until my senior year of high school. I was in Puerto Vallarta, Mexico, doing a study abroad program for my senior year. I started feeling differently not long after I arrived.

What were the signs and symptoms that you first experienced?

Well, at first, honestly I thought maybe I was just a little homesick. I was constantly feeling under the weather with sore throats, exhaustion, and just generally feeling unwell. I kind of felt like it might be a little "in my head," but the constant exhaustion and lack of energy were definitely not like me.

Then, fast forward two years, I was a sophomore at Boston University and just trying to enjoy being a "typical" 18-year-old and I got mono. Now, I knew that mono was common among college students and young adults, but I hadn't kissed anyone. I hadn't been sharing drinks. Nothing I had done could explain where it came from. And after three weeks of trying to fight off the symptoms, I knew I was never going to be the same person again.

The symptoms started out very flu-like, but they quickly

progressed to things like numbness in the extremities and neuropathy. It started in my toes, working its way up to my feet, and then into my legs, hips, and eventually throughout my entire body. At that time, I didn't know what "neuropathy" was so I would just say, "my legs are asleep."

Then, I went on another study abroad program, this time in Sydney, Australia. One day, I was sitting in this beautiful park in Sydney, spending some time with my friends. When I went to get up to leave, I couldn't get up.

My legs were completely asleep.

I couldn't stand.

I couldn't move.

I was frozen.

It was at this point that I knew something was seriously wrong.

Then, my memory started to fail me. I would find myself sitting in classes, eager to ask a question. The professor would call on me and I'd ask my question, only to forget and a few moments later, find myself raising my hand and asking the same question again. It was pretty embarrassing because I was a smart kid. Now suddenly I couldn't remember more than a few moments at a time.

The other problem was with meeting new people. I'd have to ask their names a couple of times to remember. Or, like, I'd forget people's names within hours of meeting them and have to wait until someone else said it so I didn't have to ask again. It became very frustrating, and along with the neuropathy, prompted me to seek medical attention and try to figure out what was going on.

Do you know where and how you contracted Lyme?

No, I don't, unfortunately. There were just so many ticks in my childhood,. My brother, my dad, my friends-- they had all had acute Lyme and were treated with no further issues. So why wouldn't I assume that I would also be fine? It could have happened at any point in my life, and I may never know.

What was your journey to getting a diagnosis like?

I went through a slew of different diagnoses and suggested issues before finding the right answer. First, they said it was mono again. Then, someone suggested IBS. Another doctor said it was autoimmune. Lupus, MS, and all the "usual" invisible illnesses came up at one point or another.

And at the same time, I was also being told that "nothing is wrong with you," so that was discouraging. All the exams, all the tests, nothing pointed to why I was having these strange and serious symptoms. So, I eventually sought out my pediatrician and general practitioner. This was the doctor that delivered me as a baby and had taken care of me my entire life. He was the first person to actually administer a Lyme disease test, which came back positive.

He prescribed doxycycline for two weeks, but I didn't get better even after the antibiotics were finished. And then, there was a moment that even he, the man who had delivered her and seen to her care all my life, didn't believe me. He didn't believe that I wasn't better or that I was still experiencing symptoms, again saying maybe it was "in my head."

I knew that something was different. But if someone so close to me didn't believe me, I must be losing my mind. Or, maybe all the doctors were right and there was really nothing wrong. In any case, it was a short stretch to that downward spiral of feeling discouraged, defeated, and like maybe I really was a little crazy. After all, no one had any real answers to offer.

Fortunately, throughout all of this, my mom was a huge advocate. She cared a lot about getting to the bottom of the situation and didn't care what the doctors said. She was going to figure this out and find a way to get her daughter the help she needed, no matter what that meant. So, she started talking to people and doing more research online, and that eventually led to me getting a longer form Lyme test.

What was your official diagnosis?

I was officially diagnosed with Lyme in 2015. I can't tell you how long I've actually had it, though. While the symptoms presented in high school and college, it could have been much earlier. I have also had all three coinfections, thyroid issues, POTS in my heart, and tons of other illnesses and issues since then.

What was your treatment journey like?

In 2016, I met Dr. Katherine Lantsman. She's made a huge impact on my Lyme disease and my life in general. We've got a really unique relationship, two strong-willed person-alities often fighting over treatments and the next course of action, but she always knew what was best. We had such a good connection and relationship that I still travel back to see her, even though I'm not living in the area.

It was also in 2016 that I started an aggressive round of oral antibiotics. I was eager to beat this and wanted to take a head-on approach, but the regimen was taking its toll on my body. I got really ill during this treatment. The first round made me really sick. I probably lost 30 to 40 pounds. The antibiotics were making me so sick that I wasn't even really getting the medicine that I needed.

So, in 2017, to counteract that and help get the medicine into my body, we decided to do a PICC line. At that time, of course, and even still today, the PICC line is a very controversial treatment for Lyme. Many doctors are still against it. My own family members were even questioning if it was a good choice.

But honestly, if you ask me, the PICC line is really what helped kick it out of my body because my body was actually getting the medication it needed.

Throughout the process, there were plenty of highs and lows. We tried many medications to no avail, exhausting tons of different treatment options. And I didn't choose to go the homeopathic route because it was way too overwhelming for me. I was in college, trying to start a career, and trying to balance a strict regimen of supplements that need to be taken at precise times. That was far too taxing, so I quickly realized that was not the route for me.

How has your life been affected by Lyme disease?

My Lyme disease diagnosis definitely impacted my college experience. I feel like I missed out on college because even though I was there, I barely remember it. Between the brain fog and being so sick, it's all a blur. I even graduated a year early so I could just be done and focus on my illness.

Missing out was hard. Feeling alone, isolated, and ashamed about having a chronic illness was just the norm. You feel like a burden. I didn't want to be a problem or a bother, so I chose to be the quiet one, which is absolutely not like me at all. It's actually a far cry from the rest of my life, where I've always been outgoing, outspoken, and very easy to socialize with others.

It's an incredibly isolating experience, and it's scary because you don't have answers to issues that you are clearly experiencing. It's draining, to say the very least.

You said your mom was an advocate; who else have you met on your journey that supports you?

My family's support, and especially my mom's, played a huge role in helping me get the right diagnosis and be able to find the right treatment options. Plus, I was fortunate that my parents could afford the out-of-pocket costs to see the best doctors and get the best answers, no matter what it took. And also, finding a good doctor that I could trust and that I feel like really listened to me made a huge difference.

I did eventually find friends and people for my support network that saw me and heard me. Not all of my friends stuck around, of course, but I have some great new ones, too. I've been with my current partner for three years. She's wonderful, and she absolutely understands and allows space for the Lyme disease. She has been a great support network and we even work together at Chronically Capable, the company I co-founded.

How has Lyme shaped your future and your goals, etc.?

Well, I think that it's helped me balance a lot of the anger and frustration with gratitude for what I've learned along the way. It also impacted my career in a huge way. A week after college graduation, I had my PICC line put in. So, that summer after college, instead of dealing with adjusting to a new career and life as an "adult," I was dealing with this major lifestyle change. I was adjusting instead to having a PICC line in my body to administer the medication that I so desperately needed. I was balancing my desire to have a career with a need to protect myself. I was also facing all the fear, shame, and stigma that came from trying to find a job when you have an invisible illness.

I moved to DC and took a job in marketing, which I loved. However, I had no idea how to disclose my illness, ask for accommodations, or anything like that. I didn't feel qualified to check the disability box on applications, so I chose to stay silent until I couldn't anymore.

I was working for a very small company with fewer than 25 employees, so they didn't have to follow ADA compliance guidelines. The boss was also not inclusive or accepting of the illness and some of the most traumatic experiences with my Lyme happened during this time, further compounding the issues. Most importantly, perhaps, was that my boss refused to allow me to have my PICC line at my desk.

So, there I was, hiding in the bathroom, the basement, or anywhere I could to administer this medication, which is really only effective when it's administered for a full eight hours a day. So, eventually, I was forced to choose between my health and a career I was passionate about.

I struggled at first, but then I started going to support groups and talking to others online, including those in the Lyme community and others with chronic illness. I learned that there are millions of people facing similar struggles with their careers and chronic illness, and that my story was not unique. And then, I found a job and a boss that changed my entire career future.

My next job was at a startup company. Unlike my first job, this time I was transparent from the beginning about my illness. My new boss, Kai, welcomed me with open arms. He grew up with an aunt that struggled with blindness and accessibility, so he was always thinking about accessibility, creating accessible workplaces, and so forth. One day, it occurred to me that there was the potential for a new business: connecting people like me, those struggling with chronic conditions, with jobs that are a good fit for their health and lifestyle needs.

After about six months, my boss and I left and founded Chronically Capable. No sooner did we plan the media blitz than I was having my PICC line removed. That first summer was a frenzy, but I'm grateful for having the resources and being able to fight back, and for having made a career out of something I'm passionate about.

How has Lyme impacted your relationships?

Well, for a long time, I just didn't have any. Even making friends was hard because I was always tired or having other symptoms, so I wasn't always able to go out, socialize, and stuff like that. I actually also chose to come out around the same time I was diagnosed with Lyme disease, so it was a bit like coming out all at once. The Lyme felt burdensome and I didn't want to put that on anyone.

For the first year and a half, I was in a really unhealthy relationship with someone who just couldn't grasp what I was dealing with. It's also difficult to figure out how and when to tell people that you have a disease like Lyme. I had a PICC line, which you can't hide, so I basically had to be upfront. And, eventually, I started seeing someone else, but when my PICC line exploded and I had to go to the hospital, the stress involved was too much and that relationship ended, too.

However, I now have a great partner- my girlfriend, she's fantastic. For me, the biggest battle came in making sure that I was taking care of someone else, but also still taking time to care for myself. My family relationships were just made stronger because they were a large part of my support network, and they still are today.

When you think about the future of Lyme, are you hopeful there is a cure?

Yes, I am, but with reservations. I think that there is more hope now than ever. COVID and its ongoing effects for many have helped draw attention to chronic illness and I feel like the world is on the brink of change.

However, I also believe that advocacy and action will go a long way in driving the culture for Lyme. There's a lot of infighting among the Lyme groups and within the community; if we could get rid of that and create a stronger desire to come together for the common good, it can only get better.

What one word would you use to sum up your Lyme story?

Resilience. It's a long, scary process and through it all, you have to be resilient if you are going to survive, let alone thrive, when you have a chronic illness like Lyme disease.

Any final thoughts?

I do want to note really quickly, as I've mentioned through-out the interview, that I had a certain level of privilege that some people don't in my Lyme diagnosis and treatment. I was fortunate to have a family that could support my needs and help me seek out doctor after doctor and treat-ment after treatment until I found what worked. I know that everyone doesn't have that kind of privilege, and I am eternally grateful that I did.

I imagine what it's like for people who don't have the financial means—fewer answers, fewer people to listen, and a much longer journey. I was fortunate that I could fire doctors that didn't fit my needs until I found the one that did. Not everyone has that kind of access and that's why we need more awareness, more research, etc.

Warrior is an *amazing* look on you

TESS WILLIAMS

Buffalo, NY

Determined

Strong

Passionate

Our second interview is from Tess, a project manager from Buffalo, New York, who has had a much longer timeline in her Lyme story. Although she first started seeing symptoms around age 12, she could have gotten it at five years old.

What are three words that describe you?

Determined, strong, and passionate. Those are the three words I would like to think describe me best.

Where did your Lyme journey begin?

I first got injured in eighth grade at basketball practice. I hurt my knee and it never got better. Then, tendonitis set in and they originally diagnosed that as Osgood Schlatter, a condition commonly seen in soccer players. By the time I was done with my freshman year of high school, I was out of all sports and had already seen tons of doctors. Up next, I went to a rheumatologist, who saw me for 30 minutes and then prescribed pain meds.

Those pain meds caused stomach issues, so they added a stomach protector that was supposed to help. Unfortunately, that almost made things worse. By the end of the summer, I was off those meds and onto the next journey. In the fall of my sophomore year, we took advantage of our proximity to Cleveland Clinic and drove in for an appointment. The doctors at this meeting spent about 10 minutes talking to me and then diagnosed me with fibromyalgia.

Upon further research, they decided that "you just need to exercise more" and sent me to a psychiatrist. The psychiatrist tried to say that I was depressed, making the symptoms up, and so forth. Fortunately, through all of it, my parents were really supportive and kept seeking out new information and new doctors when we weren't getting the right answers.

Do you know where and how you contracted Lyme?

I have no idea where my Lyme came from or when I contracted it. As a kid, I loved playing outdoors, camping, and running through the woods with my friends. I came home covered in bug bites all the time and I wouldn't have known to check for ticks even if there were one.

I also never got the trademark rash, and had been tested three or four times for Lyme and gotten false negatives. However, I'm pretty sure a lot of that has to do with the fact that the approved test for Lyme in New York is only about 20% accurate.

We didn't even know to question things or consider Lyme disease as a potential cause at first. And when the symptoms first appeared, they thought maybe this was it, but all the tests came back negative and not all the symptoms matched.

What was your journey to a diagnosis like?

I ended up going on medical leave at the end of my sophomore year. I caught up on my coursework over the summer and went back to school in the fall. I had to drop down from advanced courses to regular courses just to keep up. I was also applying for colleges at this time, and was accepted into Cornell, which is where I went for hotel management.

Before college started, I attended one of those wilderness bonding events with other students. We lived in the wilderness for a week, getting to know each other and learning how to help and support one another. I returned from the trip without incident, and then about two weeks into the semester, my legs gave out. I was still suffering from joint pain, fatigue, brain fog, and other symptoms, and this new symptom added another scary layer to the mystery.

I was living on campus at that point and managed to crawl across the hall to my roommate's door to get help. She called for help, which resulted in my going to the hospital and having a barrage of tests performed. That, of course, was only to be told that "nothing was wrong" yet again. Then, about two weeks later, I woke up with sprained knees after not having done anything. Their solution was to give me knee braces to wear for the rest of the semester. That didn't actually help much.

I started missing classes because physically, I was unable to get there. Some of my professors were supportive, but I had one who wasn't. I was trying my hardest to tough it out, despite the pain and other symptoms. By the spring semester, I was back on medical leave. I'd seen nearly three dozen doctors at this point and wasn't optimistic about the future. However, with the support of my parents, I did keep pushing for answers. That resulted in eventually getting a more accurate Lyme test, which came back positive.

How many doctors have you seen?

Leading up to my freshman year of college, I had seen at least 30 doctors. Then, there were a few more after that in trying to figure out how to treat the chronic symptoms of Lyme. The most supportive doctor was my naturopath, who is also an MD and familiar with chronic Lyme symptoms. Not only did she know how to identify Lyme, but she knew how to come up with an effective treatment plan.

How long have you had Lyme disease?

Starting from when I first got symptoms, it's been almost 20 years. However, I could have had Lyme for a lot longer.

What was your Lyme treatment plan like?

The plan created by my naturopath included nutritional IVs, a special diet, antibiotics, and other medications, and all just so that I could function sort of "normally." We created this plan together and tweaked it as we went along to make sure that it was doing as much as possible for my symptoms.

Once my Lyme was diagnosed, I started on an aggressive treatment regimen that included six days of outpatient care each week, including antibiotics, nutritional therapy, and other care. My symptoms initially got worse instead of better, despite taking seven or eight different antibiotics, including doxycycline, to no avail. After about a year and a half of treatment with the naturopath, I realized I wasn't going to be able to return to Cornell. I was crushed, but enrolled in Niagara University and stayed in Buffalo to be close to my family.

Then, suddenly, about halfway through the first semester, I somehow went into remission. My symptoms were just gone- no more pain, no brain fog, nothing. So, I decided to petition and reapply to Cornell. I wasn't sure why the symptoms went away or how long they'd stay gone, but I wanted to finish college. I returned to Cornell and graduated without further issues.

Mind you, I was still on antibiotics, oxygen therapies, and about two hours of various treatments per day to function. But I was functioning. So, if something hurt or bothered me, I would kind of sweep it under the rug and assume that it's "just part of life now." And after about two years, I was feeling good about where I was at and decided to take a job in Florida.

A year into the Florida job and I started gaining and losing weight. I was having circulation issues, joint pain, migraines, and several other symptoms. I didn't think back to Lyme disease because I had been treated and told I was fine. I opted to move back to Buffalo again and started working for one of my dad's companies. After being home for about six months, I woke up one morning, completely paralyzed.

Head to toe, I couldn't move.

Slowly, deliberately, I inched my way to the phone on the stand by my bed and called my parents. They came immediately and realized that there was still a big need for more help. That's when we eventually found Envita Medical Center in Scottsdale, but even that took another five doctors.

I had to break up the treatments in Scottsdale because they were so harsh on my body. I went to Envita three or four times and was fortunate to have my mom and other family and friends to keep me company while I was there. I get nutritional IVs and other treatments here in Buffalo, but I still travel to Scottsdale about once a year. I've also found some success with stem cell therapy, oxygen therapies for my joint pain, and methylene blue, which was given to me to treat brain fog.

I also currently have a gluten-free diet that is as organic as possible and I try to live organically, too. That includes organic laundry detergent, etc. I also run three or four times a week and use cryotherapy and Epsom salt baths to ease the joint pain.

What kind of family support have you had throughout your Lyme journey?

I am so, so very lucky to have a supportive family, including parents who are financially and emotionally available for whatever I need. They assist with paying for treatments, making sure that I get the care I need, and allowing me to live as normal of a life as possible. They have helped extensively in finding the right doctors, including my current doctor.

I was also fortunate to be able to get a job working for one of my father's companies. I started working in the project management side of things at a construction company, which makes taking the time I need to deal with my health easy and gives me the flexibility that I need. When I was at Envita, my mom would come to visit about once a month; she couldn't stay because of work, but the fact that she came out that much was just super supportive.

What kind of emotional toll has Lyme taken on your life and your relationships?

Lyme definitely impacted me emotionally. I put my dating life completely on hold and I felt very isolated throughout the entire experience. Even though I had the support of my family and close friends, I missed out on a lot of the "typical" college stuff because I was just too tired or couldn't move to get out to parties and events in the first place.

I definitely feel like I was robbed of my college experience. I felt alone, like I was a burden to those around me, and started struggling with anxiety and depression. I had that feeling that most of us eventually do: "Am I crazy? Maybe this really IS all in my head…"

It was difficult to feel like I couldn't be independent. However, I also feel that some good things come from the worst parts of your life. I think I've developed more empathy, more sarcasm, and a better attitude about life in general.

How has Lyme impacted your future or shaped your life?

Although Lyme affected my college experience and kept me from a lot of the things I loved, it also helped me meet some of my own personal goals. Admittedly, I was never going to be a star athlete, but I was always very competitive. I had always wanted to compete in something. After all the issues with my Lyme, I had heard about a 5K that was happening down the street from my apartment in Florida. I figured it wouldn't be too difficult to walk, so I signed up and walked the entire 5K.

A couple of days later, there was a 10K, so I signed up and walked that. From there, I was hooked. I went on to run a 5K, then a 10K, and then did the Disney Princess Weekend half-marathon challenge. I also did the Dopey Challenge, a weekend event covering four days:

- Thursday: 5K
- Friday: 10K
- Saturday: Half-Marathon
- Sunday: Full Marathon

After every run, I felt better than I ever had when battling my Lyme disease. And when I finished the Dopey Challenge, the Global Lyme Alliance contacted me asking if I'd like to run the New York City Marathon on their behalf. At the end of that race, a friend asked me which was more painful: Lyme disease or running a marathon. I answered without hesitation: definitely Lyme.

Of course, I did have to shift my career dreams a bit. Originally, I wanted to be the President of Disney World. But being on my feet was becoming an increasingly apparent issue. At this time, I was working in hospitality and running a hotel, but when my symptoms got worse, I started doing more admin stuff. This led me to start thinking about working in development because I could work remotely, be on my feet less often, and apply all the operations experience I had to something that I could enjoy.

This is where my family came to the rescue once again, and how I came to my current position in project management. It also allows me the time that I need to make my visits to Scottsdale and lets me be close to family for support.

How were your personal relationships affected by Lyme?

In addition to not having the typical college experience and being worried about being judged, I kept quiet and didn't make a lot of friends during that time. As adults, it's been a little easier, but there are also people who say things like, "Well you can run, so you're not that sick."

Dating was way too much of a hassle. I didn't date in college because, in addition to the Lyme issues I was having, I was also feeling like a burden and didn't want to have to figure out how to explain things to someone or find a supportive partner. I haven't even really worried about dating and at this point, I'm more focused on my career and enjoying my own life first. I'll worry about dating and settling down in the future.

Who have you met along your journey that has had a positive impact?

Samantha Stonerook, my patient care coordinator from Envita, has been my support and my rock in more ways than I can count. She is always there for me and has made my time in Scottsdale less lonely, too.

Then, there's my roommate from Florida, Summer Zacker (now Rowan). At the time she had been diagnosed with fi-bromyalgia, but as soon as I heard her story, I was like, "you have Lyme." We met almost by accident. Even though we're both from Buffalo, Summer is a few years younger than me. We connected almost instantly when we met in Florida. When I suggested Lyme, Summer completely balked at the idea, so I just let it go. About six months later, I got a text from Summer saying she did indeed have Lyme.

Since we were both going through it, we were able to bond over our treatments, symptoms, allergies, and all the other issues that come along with having Lyme disease.

Are you hopeful that there will be a cure for Lyme in the future?

Yes. However, I want to point out that I don't think that a "cure" will be in the form of some singular magic treat-ment. I think that additional research and awareness will lead to insights into finding the best course of treatments or set of therapies that are most effective. I'm also hopeful that better tools and testing will continue to spur earlier diagnosis and treatment, which can often alleviate the risk of chronic, lifelong Lyme symptoms.

"I have seen at least 30 doctors"
A far too common response from
Chronic Lyme patients

GENNY BROWN

Surry, UK

Tenacious

Loyal

Joyful

Our next story comes from Genny Brown, a biochemist living in Surrey, in the United Kingdom, about an hour outside of London. The UK has even less information about Lyme than we do in the U.S. and the NHS has even denied that Lyme is a chronic disease, which makes it that much more difficult to find treatment and support for the condition.

What are three words that describe you?

I would say tenacious, very loyal, and joyful. I'm always laughing, always have a smile. I even have an angry laugh, apparently, according to my friends.

Is there a song that has inspired you or helped on your journey?

I can't even tell you that I have one specific genre that I love, I tend to dip in and out. So I can't say I really have one song, but music is definitely important to me.

Can you tell me a little bit about where you are now and where your journey began?

I am currently located in Surrey, about an hour from London. I was living in London proper until a couple of years ago when work went hybrid because of COVID-19. I decided it was time to get out of the city and into the green spaces where I could relax, breathe, and manage my stress more effectively. It's done wonders for my mental health and my Lyme symptoms.

I was born in Aruba to Dutch-Aruban parents and moved to the UK about 15 years ago. One day, I was washing my hair and a huge section of it came out in my hands, right from the roots. Naturally, I freaked out. I called my mom first, who was still living in Aruba at the time. She urged me to go see a doctor about it, so I did.

Unfortunately, that first doctor was very calm and casual, asking about life, stress, and other issues. Finally, he suggested that it's probably "just dry scalp." I felt very dismissed and pushed out the door. On top of this sudden loss of hair, I was overwhelmed and unsure of what to do next.

This was also when I started to have more anxiety, and then I started to experience brain fog and aphasia, completely forgetting words I knew in regular conversation all the time. Eventually, I started forgetting entire conversations. I was always so organized, focused, and on-point that even my colleagues were starting to notice that it was unlike me and I was starting to realize that something really wasn't right.

I had been a fairly healthy person to this point. I didn't get sick a lot and I'm not the type of person to panic or turn something into nothing. I had been signed off work for "stress" because I could barely get out of bed some days, but there was no real diagnosis at this point. That would require a very long road of talking to people who didn't have answers, let alone those who didn't seem to want to listen in the first place.

Do you know where your Lyme disease was contracted?

I am fairly certain that I can identify when and how I got Lyme, although I didn't know it at the time. When I was 31, I went on holiday to Turkey. I was hiking on one of the islands near Istanbul. I remember being bitten by something, assuming it was probably a spider, and moving on. I had a touch of a fever but no real "bite" or rash, and then I was fine. This happened in 2013.

At the time, I was working for an Italian oil company. I had several friends, an active church life, and plenty of other life things keeping me busy. I was also at a point in my career where I could afford to travel more and was enjoying that part of my 30s. However, about three months later, I started experiencing my first symptoms and sought medical attention to figure out what was going on. I didn't initially think about the holiday at first, but upon further questioning, I realized that it could very well have been the point of infection.

What was your diagnostic journey like?

I guess I was fortunate, in some ways, because after I didn't get anywhere with the first visit, I scheduled another appointment with my GP. However, she was out on maternity leave and they had brought in a locum. This particular doctor was experienced in infectious diseases. She was also experienced enough in her field to notice the change in my history.

She looked and noticed that I had been in very little in the past, and then suddenly, I was here every month experiencing any number of symptoms. That led her to conclude that I must have some type of infectious tropical disease. She immediately questioned my travel, at which point I glossed over my visit to Turkey but I did mention I was from Aruba. This led her to send me to the School of Tropical Medicine.

Finally, there was some hope. At this point, I was so fatigued I could barely get out of bed. Friends and others were coming in to help with cooking and cleaning, and the fatigue set in so easily that I wasn't sure I'd be able to find hope. Then I met this doctor and it felt like finally, someone was going to listen.

At the School of Tropical Medicine, I saw a very well-known doctor who sent me for a barrage of tests. Then, he said that I might just be suffering from viral fatigue and that I might need to be on antibiotics for the rest of my life. He told me I should learn to accept that I may never actually get to the bottom of what's wrong. He even suggested finding work that was less intense because I could no longer sustain the life I once had. And sitting there at just 33 or 34 years old, hearing this information, I was unwilling to accept it.

I'm not sure what broke inside of my brain, but I just blurted out to the doctor, "I'm sorry, but that's unacceptable." They were telling me I was going to need lifelong antibiotics, which is not sustainable. And what else can that open the door to, in terms of future symptoms or issues? We had a bit more discussion and then he asked what I did. I told him I was a biochemist. He told me I was the "worst kind of patient" because I was educated and thought I knew more than him, who had been doing this for years and had been properly trained, and so forth.

But I knew my body. I knew something was not okay. And most importantly, I knew his solution of putting a bandage on the problem was not going to get to the root of the issue, or get results. So, when I returned to my GP, naturally I relayed the experience and my GP was completely furious and at a loss.

At this point, my GP advised me that she couldn't officially tell me to try the naturopathic route, but that it might be a good idea to start exploring other options beyond conventional medicine. I think this was the most pivotal point in my entire journey. My research on naturopathic providers led me to one of the official centers for the diagnosis of Lyme disease in the UK. I met a provider with a background in infectious diseases. I originally chose them because they have a lot of alternative resources like dieticians and so forth. And thinking that it was related to allergies or some other issue, it seemed like that type of facility would be able to help me come up with an effective treatment.

My initial consultation was very short, but this time it wasn't dismissive. The doctor I saw advised me that I needed to see another doctor there to confirm the diagnosis. When that doctor reviewed my case and discussed my symptoms, she said it was glaringly obvious that it was Lyme disease. However, she of course ordered a test to be sure, which came back positive.

Finally, I had an answer. However, that also came with a certain amount of shock, because I learned that with everything I'd been through in the past three years, every test I'd been given, the one thing they didn't test for was Lyme. There's also a lot of contention around testing in the UK because their methods are mostly outdated and archaic. Most people end up with false negatives unless they can afford to have tests sent out to the U.S. or Germany.

My test was sent to Germany, and I am aware that I was fortunate to be able to pay to have the test sent away. I know that not everyone is so fortunate, which makes it that much harder to get an accurate diagnosis. At this time, I was also struggling with some depression, though, because the full weight of what had really been going on was hitting me.

I wasn't crazy. I wasn't losing my mind and it wasn't "all in my head." It was Lyme disease, and it had been, all along.

How many doctors did you see throughout the course of your diagnosis and treatment journey?

It took 10 doctors over the course of three years before I got an answer. I was in bed all the time, even napping around my morning routine to make it to work before I was put on leave. I was often suffering in silence because I didn't want to bother trying to make my friends understand what I was going through, and I was already at a disadvantage in my highly competitive industry as a black woman, so I didn't want to be tainted as the "sick person," too.

What kind of family support have you had throughout this journey?

Much of my family is still back in Aruba. However, they have always been supportive, even from the beginning with my mom urging me to continue to get care, to continue to ask questions, seek answers, and to keep pushing to know more. They didn't really understand how bad it really had gotten because they were so far away. My mom came to visit one time and she even told me she could tell that I wasn't "Genny" anymore. However, after the fact, I think it's brought us closer.

Is your doctor supportive?

Not only is my doctor supportive, but she's also been doing tons more research into Lyme disease, including things like the neurological effects so that she can be a better provider. It's great, really.

What was your treatment journey like?

My treatment and diagnostic journey are largely interwoven because I underwent many of the wrong treatments and attempted to get care for many incorrect diagnoses over the years. Countless cycles of antibiotics did little to help. The first doctor put me on antibiotics for three months. In the first month, things got a little better. The second month, I couldn't keep any food down and was so sick that I'd lost a ton of weight. And by the third month, I was scared to take the antibiotics because I didn't want to lose more weight or feel sick, so I just quit taking them mostly.

When I finally met with the naturopath, she told me that it was good they blasted my body with antibiotics, but that wasn't good enough. My body was in such a stressed condition and it was essentially just reacting to everything that was being thrown at it. She decided to simplify my diet to remove anything that could be causing or exacerbating the issues I was having. That meant a strict gluten-free, highly organic diet that was almost vegan in its simplicity.

After three months, they started reintroducing different foods to help establish eating habits for the future. At the same time, she put me on ToxaPrevent, a German medication designed to help detox the body from heavy metals, mold, and other bacteria. The idea was to help my digestive system by giving the liver, kidneys, and gut a chance to breathe and get an intensive detox, of sorts.

I also had to learn how to get the right nutrients through supplementation. I was privileged, again, to be able to do so with trial and error. However, that privilege doesn't remove the fear. It was a scary time, for sure. The final recommendation that my doctor had was to rest. When the body is tired, she told me, you rest. When you feel like you can't, don't. Listen to your body and allow it to recover, mentally, physically, and otherwise.

Throughout all of this, over the course of about eight months, I started to feel better. After a year, I was about 75% back to the person I was before Lyme. Currently, I am taking the least amount of supplements and medications that I ever have, and I only have mild bouts of fatigue once or twice a year. I do still struggle with memory issues and aphasia, which is extra frustrating because I speak five languages and when I lose a word, I lose it in all of them.

I meet with my naturopath about once a year. I also do my own research, take high-quality supplements, and continue with my strict gluten-free diet that is as organic as it can get.

What kind of effect did Lyme have on your emotional well-being?

During the diagnosis process, I often found myself feeling discouraged, disheartened, and like no one was listening. I was depressed and almost started believing the doctors that were saying it was all in my head or that I was making things up. I also still have a lot of fear and anxiety surrounding my condition. To this day, even the slightest feeling of a symptom causes me to get anxious and wonder if there's a flare-up coming.

I also felt like I had to keep fighting because I wasn't willing to accept that there "may never be an answer." That wasn't good enough for me. To a certain degree, my anxiety almost fueled that fighting spirit and helped me get to a place where I could get a diagnosis and some treatment. However, it also isolated me and caused me to lead a double life, of sorts. I didn't want to let people know what was really going on or how serious my condition was. I spent many years struggling with shame and uncertainty, and trying to find someone to listen, accept me, and help me find answers.

How has Lyme changed your life and shaped your future?

I have had to change a lot of my lifestyle due to Lyme. I have to follow a very strict diet these days, and I still take a lot of medications to keep the most debilitating symptoms at bay. Whenever I feel a chill or another symptom, I get anxious about another attack, so there's a lot of struggle with anxiety related to that. I also no longer have the focus I once did for reading, which I loved. I have since learned to enjoy audiobooks and podcasts and even come to love TV.

In 2017, I got really into personal training. This has had a positive effect on my life and my future, leading me to do a polar expedition alongside others without Lyme, learning a lot about my own condition and tenacity along the way. I was even put up to doing a solo expedition by the world's leading guide, Doug Stoup. He asked why I did the original expedition and what it would mean to the Lyme community for me to complete the solo journey. He got excited and that got me excited. So, when he wouldn't stop asking me about it, I finally agreed. He gifted me the harness that I use today to pull tires because he wanted me to believe that I could do this.

Now, I get up at 4:00 AM to get to the gym by 5:00 AM. I do an hour and a half of strength training and some cardio. Then, I spend an hour and a half dragging a tire around on my lunch, and do some stretching and recovery in the evening. Fridays are for recovery exercises and Saturdays are for rest. Sunday, I'll go out and spend six or seven hours pulling a tire all around the woods and this path by my house. In a polar expedition, you're skiing uphill for eight or 10 hours and pulling a sled, so you need to have that endurance.

I am also fortunate because the people in my life know about my condition and how it impacts my capabilities and how I train. I am also the only black woman to do the expedition and the other one did it guided. I didn't have to deal with a lot of discrimination and racism in Aruba, so it didn't often occur to me that I was a minority, but I felt like this was a good way to advocate for myself and the Lyme community.

How were your personal relationships impacted by Lyme?

I had to put my dating life mostly on hold for three years trying to find a diagnosis. I didn't want to be a burden, and I didn't want to deal with trying to explain this invisible illness to someone. And when I eventually did get around to seeing someone, they didn't understand the situation. It was just easier to stay single and focus on my recovery. This disease did propel me to embrace self-care and gave me the space to be able to say, "this is who I am now and there are times when I'll be okay and times when I won't."

It made the way I choose partners very different. I knew that I needed someone who was kind, understanding, and compassionate, but I also knew that wasn't easy to find. My most recent relationship ended because we simply decided we were better off friends. There wasn't any bad blood, and he was always a great support. In fact, he still is, and even used to defend me to my friends.

And speaking of friends, I'm lucky to have had a strong network of them to be there for me through all of this. I had friends bringing food, cooking and cleaning, and helping in many different ways. And although my family was further away and didn't quite realize just how serious my condition was, once they did I think it brought us closer and helped make us all a bit more understanding of each other all around.

Are you hopeful for a cure?

Yes, I am hopeful that there is a cure in the future. I also hope that there is more research and funding to support that. I only spent three years fighting to get a diagnosis, but I know some people who spend 10 or 15 years or more trying to get to the bottom of it. For all of us, I am hopeful that the future holds more in terms of both treatments and an eventual cure.

What advice do you have for the Lyme community?

Do not let the illness define you, despite how debilitating and limiting it can be at times. Instead of day by day, take it moment by moment. Let bad moments happen knowing that good moments will come. Celebrate the good and rest when you need to. We need more of that as a society in general-- rest and peace could do wonders for us all.

Celebrate The Good

TODD SMITH

London, UK

Passionate

Determined

Vulnerable

Todd Smith lives on a canal boat just outside of London in the United Kingdom. For him, being on the water and connected to nature is very healing. His story is a bit brief, but still worthy of telling because it offers yet another perspective of Lyme. Even as we began the interview, Todd relayed to me about the year or so that he spent scared to go into the woods or tall grasses, and how he now has a deep connection with nature that's become one of his most healing attributes.

What are three words that describe you?

I am passionate, determined, and vulnerable.

Do you have a song that's inspired you on your journey?

One that comes to mind is called "Spirit" by Xavier Rudd.

Where did your Lyme journey begin?

Right before the COVID pandemic, in the fall of 2019, I started experiencing knee pain. I had already been medically grounded from flying due to gut health issues, after spending seven years to become a pilot, which was my life's dream. I had a personal trainer, and so the knee pain I initially attributed to maybe pushing myself a little too hard in my workouts.

Not long after I started having knee pain, I also noticed a small rash developing on the inside of my left leg. I know now that it was the "trademark" bullseye rash that Lyme is known for, but at the time it didn't look like anything I'd seen before. And Lyme isn't as widely known in the UK either, so I was never even looking for or thinking about ticks.

It's interesting, actually... I am admittedly a bit of a worrier and my first thought upon seeing this strange rash was that I might have skin cancer or something of the like. So after a couple of weeks, I decided to make an appointment to see my GP and get it checked out.

Do you know where and how you contracted Lyme disease?

I do, yes. I was able to trace back the timeline from when the rash and knee pain started, and figured out when it happened. I was in the park in central London, visiting with an old school friend. We were having a good visit and it was a nice day, so I was wearing shorts and enjoying sitting in the grass. I never felt a tick or a bite, so I didn't make any connection until much later when the symptoms appeared.

What was your journey to getting a diagnosis like?

Once I went to my GP, they took one look at the rash and knew that it was indicative of Lyme disease. They performed a test, which came back positive, and then I was put on antibiotics. I was relieved that it wasn't skin cancer, but then I didn't know much about Lyme disease or how it worked. So I started doing my own research to learn about the potential for long-term effects and symptoms.

I was already a bit reluctant about the antibiotics because I'd been on them before. I had been grounded from flying because of my gut microbiome issues and antibiotics didn't help that. I was also dealing with some stomach troubles and was about six months sober at the time, so I felt maybe this was some sort of stress manifesting itself and coming out in my body. However, the doctor confirmed that it was, in fact, Lyme disease.

What was your treatment journey like?

My treatment began with antibiotics, and I guess as is the case with most people, my symptoms got worse before they got better. I lost a lot of mental clarity to the brain fog, and I was really worried about how this could impact my career. At just under 30, I couldn't fathom giving up my life and career, and I was a bit terrified.

I started to experience worsening knee pain and a couple instances of heart palpitations. Because I had a family history, including a grandfather who died of a heart attack at 55, I was especially concerned about the potential effects of the Lyme and the antibiotics on my heart. By the end of the first round of antibiotics, I was still experiencing all my symptoms and some even continued to get worse.

I was very reluctant and I wasn't seeing much in the way of results, but I tried to trust the process. The symptoms continued to worsen and they told me that the next option was IV antibiotics. I didn't like that answer, for so many reasons, so I instead decided to visit the University of London. I decided that I was going to see the tropical disease specialists, who are normally only available by appointment.

I walked up to the front desk and somehow managed to charm the lady at the desk into letting me in to see those specialists. I was seen by a provider who I felt that I could trust and that would listen to me and my concerns. She basically told me that they are an authority on Lyme and can tell him that he's had more than enough antibiotics and he will be fine. It's known that symptoms get worse before they get better, and that's okay.

Today, I do feel that I've recovered from Lyme disease. I feel that that's largely due to my lifestyle, along with the early diagnosis and treatment. I was already living a vegan lifestyle, not drinking, and working with a personal trainer, so I was already in fairly good health. I was also on several supplements for my gut health issues, so I had that going for me. Plus, I'm a firm believer in "mind over matter" so that worked well for me in this situation. I could've given into the panic and fear and had a different experience entirely, but I didn't.

How long was it from diagnosis to treatment?

All told, my experience was only about three months from the time of getting an accurate diagnosis and finding the right treatment and getting back to my life. It was a short journey and for that I'm grateful, but I'm also anxious for the future and the potential that symptoms could return or long-term effects of Lyme could appear.

What kind of toll did Lyme (including diagnosis and treatment) take on your mental and emotional health?

Well, I already have a complex medical history and a bit of anxiety about my state of health, so something like Lyme was definitely scary. And not only did the Lyme cause its own anxiety, but it created worry about the symptoms that might become debilitating or that the condition could worsen over time.

Because my experience was so brief, I don't think I had a lot of time to properly deal with the emotions of having Lyme and how it impacted me personally, but I do know that I felt isolated and alone. For me, it was more of an emotional awakening, of sorts. I felt like nature wanted me to know that Lyme disease is an issue and that something needs to be done about it. I'm an activist for climate change, so this story allows me to share with others and be a voice for those who are affected.

What kind of support did you have throughout your Lyme journey?

My GP was a great resource for my Lyme disease diagnosis. She was able to prescribe and follow up on the antibiotics and make sure that I got the best treatment. However, I didn't really want to engage in the community or seek out support at first. I didn't want to engage the fear in my own mind by diving down the rabbit hole and learning about what others had experienced. So there wasn't really a ton of support there, but then I didn't really have much of a need for it, thankfully.

How has Lyme shaped you and your future?

I will be the first to tell you that I probably haven't really reflected deeply on how Lyme impacted my life. The timing was weird; this all happened in the middle of the pandemic and everything else I had going on. Today, I am well and I don't feel that I suffer from Lyme anymore. I haven't completely processed everything because of how it all happened so quickly, but I'm starting to reflect a bit on how my experience has shaped my life up to this point.

I do hope that sharing my story will help at least one person relate or feel like they're not alone in what they're going through.

Do you believe there is hope for a cure?

Yes, I do believe that there is hope for a cure for Lyme at some point. However, I do think that because of the lack of information and available resources, it will probably get much worse before it gets better.

KATIE NOLAN

London, UK

Fun

Outgoing

Hardworking

Katie is an occupational therapist based in London who is fun, outgoing, hard-working person. Or she was, that is, before she contracted Lyme. Despite all her struggles and nearly eight years of fighting for a diagnosis, she remains optimistic and hopeful for not only her future, but the future of everyone affected by Lyme disease.

What are three words that describe you?

Fun, outgoing, and hard worker, I would say.

When did your Lyme journey begin? When did you first notice symptoms?

I was 21 and had just finished university in Liverpool. I was about to go traveling, which is something I'd always wanted to do, and I started getting weird symptoms. I had a rash, but it didn't look like the typical Lyme disease rash. I was getting muscle pains and aches, headaches, and so forth.

I went to the GP and they said it was shingles or some other virus and very much just brushed it, and me, off at the time. I had my blood taken and they gave me something for the "shingles or viral whatever" but I don't remember what it was. I do remember that the pain just wasn't going away. The joint pain was becoming chronic, so I was referred to a rheumatologist. When I went to see the rheumatologist, I was told I had fibromyalgia.

I was shocked, because I was so young and healthy. How could I be given this diagnosis? But at the same time, at least here in the UK, when a doctor gives you a diagnosis, you kind of believe them. From then on, it began to spiral. I went to see all kinds of specialists because it just kept getting worse and worse. They did give me pain medication for the joint pain, but I didn't want to take too much of it because it was opioids and other medications that made me drowsy. And when I did take it, it never really alleviated all the pain.

I was also feeling a bit like, this has to be a made-up label; how can you even tell? That was my gut reaction - when I saw the rheumatologist, he actually just tapped my joints and was like, "Is this painful? Does this hurt?" And then he was like, "Okay, you've got fibromyalgia." Then, he gave me my letter and it felt like I was very brushed off. There was no follow-up suggested, just kind of a "deal with it" attitude.

I felt really dismissed and quite sad, actually. I was young and healthy, or so I thought, you know? I was depressed, and became quite anxious, as well.

At this same time, I was about to do a mental health placement in Sri Lanka. But I was worried about how I would be able to cope if my own health was all over the place.

I can't just go to see a doctor on the other side of the world.

It's so much more complicated than that. Plus managing all the symptoms... It was frustrating and anxiety inducing. And when I was expressing these frustrations to my GP, they were immediately like, "Oh, you've got panic attacks. Your anxiety is really bad. Maybe you should see a counselor or take some antidepressants or anxiety medications."

I did take something for my anxiety, which eased some of it, but it obviously wasn't getting to the root cause. It was a lot of guesswork and gaslighting that this was "something in my head" because they couldn't find an answer for the physical symptoms.

How long was it from the time you started seeing symptoms until you were diagnosed?

It was about seven years, all told. It started when I was 21 and I got officially diagnosed in April 2022, when I was 28. And in that time, it was everything from issues with my stomach like IBS to gynecological issues, and even a diagnosis of FND (functional neurological disorder) because of the brain fog, memory issues, and speech issues.

It was never really a "progression" of symptoms so much as it was an increase of different incidents- first joint pain, then brain fog and neurological issues. Then came stomach issues. Then maybe it was endometriosis. None of this ever came with any treatment or real plan, until I got my final diagnosis in April 2022.

Were you doing any research on your own to figure out what was going on?

Not really. I was just taking the medications that they gave me. Nothing really clicked about the Lyme disease until much later on. I didn't really know about it that much, to be honest, so I didn't know to start looking on my own. I trusted the doctors, mostly.

What other symptoms have you experienced?

Along with the neurological disorders, I lost much of my speech ability. My voice completely changed. I forgot words I knew and couldn't remember how to articulate my thoughts. I was having five to six seizures per day but couldn't communicate what was going on.

What was your official diagnosis? How did you find it?

I had an inpatient stay at a neuro hospital during the height of my seizures. When I came out of hospital, my cousin from Ireland tagged me on a piece of research or something about Lyme and said, "You really should get tested." She also had Lyme, and was connected to the support groups and forums online. She said there were so many others discussing similar FND-type symptoms but they really have Lyme and it just hasn't been properly diagnosed.

So, I went to the London Clinic of Nutrition and they ran a full test. It came back positive. My official diagnosis was for Lyme disease, as well as the bartonella and mycoplasma coinfections. It was a relief to finally have a diagnosis and evidence that I haven't just been going mad the past six or seven years. I finally had somewhere to go, which brought a certain degree of happiness.

Dr. Lambert in Dublin is an infectious disease doctor and is who my cousin saw. I booked a flight and went to see him for my Lyme treatment. He confirmed the diagnosis and put me on a strict regimen of oral antibiotics that I've been on for about six months now. I've got six months to go.

What is your treatment/care routine like?

In addition to the three antibiotics that I take, I also have a lot of supplements and vitamins that I take daily. I use the sauna, charcoal therapy, lemon water- all the detoxing methods that are suggested for those with Lyme and other chronic illnesses. My first six months, I was bed bound. I was still having seizures and really bad symptoms, and my mom is taking care of me, along with my sister and brother.

I was working up until last year when my seizures happened, but I haven't been able to return to work. Right now, I'm trying to focus on taking care of myself, trying to make the most of this situation. In that regard, I am also in therapy and seeing someone regularly to deal with the emotional issues.

Dr. Lambert was great. He wanted to make sure that I viewed Lyme disease as a holistic treatment approach. He wanted to make sure I didn't think it was just antibiotics and then you're cured. He urged me to get as much help as I could and I think that's really benefited me. He advised me to get all the therapy I could through the NHS, so I now have physiotherapy and speech and language therapy to assist with those issues.

I am not taking any medications for the seizures. They were diagnosed as functional seizures, which means they aren't epileptic or related to another condition. Dr. Lambert also reassured me that as the bacterial load decreased, so would the seizures. Now, I have maybe one or two every couple of weeks.

How has this affected your family?

Well, my mom is really supportive. She asks questions, she is researching it online, and so forth. She also had to largely give up working to look after me. She was working full-time, then went down to like one day a week because I needed her full-time care. My siblings have struggled watching me have seizures and all these health issues, feeling powerless because they can't do anything about it. However, through it all, they've been supportive and helpful.

How has Lyme affected you emotionally?

It's frustrating. That's the biggest word about this Lyme journey: frustration.

I **want to** work.

I **want to** live.

I **want to** have a purpose.

But this disease makes that very difficult.

It's also very isolating, which led to a lot of anxiety and depression. Losing my ability to communicate was debilitating. I was so envious of everyone else who had the ability to walk properly, and even like, just be able to pick something up. You don't realize until you're in it just how bad it is.

I have been focused on yoga, meditation, and mindfulness. As I said, I'm trying to use this period to really connect with myself and get enjoyment from recovery and relearning how to be independent. I really want my life back. I don't want to just accept this diagnosis as my life now. There are certainly some days (probably many) where you wake up and you're like, I don't want to do this. What's the point in trying?

But then, you're like, "No, Katie, you have to get up!"

You have to take your medications.

You have to do this.

Because every day of making yourself go through the motions gets you one step closer to a day when you don't have to do that.

What have you missed out on because of Lyme disease?

Travel plans have completely gone out the window. I've always wanted to go traveling but haven't been able to. Enjoying your twenties- missed that. Dating, going to parties, socializing, etc. has all been put on hold because I haven't been able to. My life always has to be planned. Everything has to be thought through, which is completely draining.

Plus, you don't really have the energy to keep explaining to people what you're dealing with, which makes it hard to make and keep friends. Luckily, I have a close-knit family and the friends that I do have are very supportive. Funnily enough, most of them work within the medical professions, so they are more than understanding about my condition, and were even before my diagnosis.

I started an Instagram, actually, called Life in Lyme Light (@lifeinlymelight), which helped me reach out to others in the community and connect with people who could support me. I also felt like a lot of the information online about Lyme disease was really bleak. I never really found anything in my research that was hopeful. It was all kind of like, 'Oh, I have Lyme disease; I'm stuck with this forever.'

From my Instagram, I wanted people to see that there is hope, there is a future, and so forth.

Are you hopeful there's a cure for Lyme? What do you think about the future?

I don't know whether "cure" is the right word, but I do think more awareness and research can lead to things like remission, and that there is definitely hope for more of all of that in the future.

How can sharing your story help others, in your opinion?

I think it's empowering. It gives us back that control and gives us that voice that was taken away by Lyme. There's still a stigma around this disease and I think that's keeping a lot of people from sharing their stories. I know for me, it was the controversy of "does she really have it?" that kept me from sharing for so long. I don't want to share my story and then have someone turn around and say it's not a thing. The NHS doesn't really know or understand Lyme here in the UK, especially, so awareness and acceptance is big.

Do you have any words of encouragement for others out there who are reading this?

Keep on going. There is hope. You might not think it now, but there is.

I want to Work

I want to Live

I want to have a Purpose

SUE SYRIANI

Athens, Greece

Positive

Energetic

Cautious

Sue Syriani has spent the past nearly 40 years living in Athens, Greece, with her husband. She grew up in South Africa, and describes herself as positive, energetic, and somewhat cautious. Unlike a lot of our stories to this point, Sue wasn't even diagnosed with Lyme until she was in her 50s. However, she certainly faced just as much adversity as the rest of us, if not more.

What are three words you would say describe you?

Positive, energetic... I would say the third one would be cautious, in a way.

Where did your Lyme journey begin?

I think it may have started when I was a child because I grew up in South Africa with horses and dogs, swimming in the river, playing outside, and such. There were ticks everywhere. My mother would de-tick me every time I got home, but no one knew about Lyme. They still don't recognize tick-borne illnesses in South Africa, as a matter of fact. As a child, I did not have any problems related to Lyme disease. However, in 2005, that all changed.

I suddenly woke up one morning with incredible joint pain and fatigue. I could hardly make it up the stairs. It was very strange for me, as I'd been active and involved in sports all my life. This sudden onset of fatigue and strange joint pains was unusual, to say the least. I thought that it would pass, so I just bore with it for a few weeks. When it didn't go away, I did start investigating.

I did have another tick bite at the end of 2003. I was hiking on an island here in Greece and had returned home to shower. I saw what I thought was a mole on my stomach.

Upon further inspection, I realized it was a tick. I removed it, threw it out, and forgot all about it. Then, in 2005, the symptoms started.

How long was it from the time symptoms appeared until you got an accurate diagnosis?

It was about eight years. I was finally diagnosed with Lyme disease after getting a test in the states in 2013. We weren't aware of Lyme or that Lyme ticks existed in Greece. In many places, they're still in denial. That made it increasingly difficult to get an accurate diagnosis and figure out what was really going on.

What was your journey to a diagnosis like?

I started doing my own research. I saw a million doctors who told me that it was all in my head. It was a long, difficult, tedious, and disappointing journey. The arthritis wasn't that surprising because of my lifetime of sports and activities, but you don't get that kind of pain overnight. It happens gradually. So I knew that something was wrong.

The first deep investigation I did here was at the naval hospital in Greece. I checked myself in for 24 hours and they did every test under the sun. At the end of it, the pathologist came in and said, "There is something wrong with you, but we don't know what it is. If you ever go to the U.S., look for this."

Then, he handed me a small piece of paper with the word "Borrelia" written on it. Of course, I just filed it away and didn't think twice about it, and it was only when I went back all those years later that I saw he was on the right track.

I was seeing a gynecologist in L.A. for some related symptoms, but he couldn't figure out what was wrong either. He referred me to an Iranian doctor in Los Angeles by the name of Dr. Paratt. I went to see him and after reviewing my case he said, "I think I know what you could have, but we need to do a lot of tests." Then, he came back with the news that I had Lyme disease. His first advice was that I look for a Lyme-literate doctor, so of course I went ahead and did that and started the next leg of the treatment journey.

It's interesting, I think, to see the difference in progress here compared to in the States. After my diagnosis in the U.S., I came back here (to Athens) and did all the tests, and they all came back negative. I specifically asked them to check for the Lyme and all its coinfections, and every test came back negative. But in the States, with IGeneX, I tested positive.

What was your treatment journey like?

Initially, I found Doctor Schaller, a Lyme-literate doctor in Florida. I flew to the States with my husband to meet him and get an initial consultation.

Fortunately, he agreed to treatment with antibiotics long-distance, because I can't stay in the U.S. indefinitely, obviously. So, we started that long journey, getting what I could here and then ordering from him overseas what we couldn't get here. My treatment regimen was all oral antibiotics; there were no injections or IVs.

I started feeling a lot better almost immediately. The joint pains eased and I started to get my life back. It was heavy going on the digestive system, though, as you can imagine.

I was doing detox, trying a variety of diets, all of which I gave up on because I'm not very disciplined. And well, quite frankly, life's too short. I did this for a couple of years until my digestive system couldn't take anymore.

After that, we did transdermal antibiotics for a short while. I applied them to my arms and legs every day, but that became time-consuming and cumbersome. So I decided to visit the Paracelsus Clinic in Switzerland, where they specialize in tick-borne diseases, cancers, etc. I spent three weeks there, on an outpatient basis. I stayed in a hotel but from 7 AM to 7 PM, I was at the clinic getting treatments.

They did colonic irrigation, ozone therapy, oxygen therapy, IV vitamins, supplements, dietary changes, basically a lot of heavy detox. I had tried chelation therapy, but that didn't suit me at all. One of the positive experiences I did have was that they had a great dentistry department at this clinic. They removed all of my root canals, which they say is a big source of bacteria and infection, and underlying health issues.

Throughout my stay, I lost nine kilos (almost 20 pounds) because of the heavy detoxing, and I was absolutely drained. I don't know how good it is to detox that much, and I don't think that I benefited much from this clinic besides the dental work.

We were in Los Angeles four times a year for many years for my husband's work. Since he's retired, it just makes sense not to travel all that distance to see doctors. We've been seeing Armin Schwarzbach in Germany. He has a lab that diagnoses and studies tick-borne diseases, and we have been doing our testing there.

How has this diagnosis affected your life?

Initially, I didn't think about it much because I didn't know much. However, the more research I did, the more I realized it was a big deal. Plus, the ignorance of the doctors over here plays a huge role in things. In the meantime, I was also diagnosed with something called MGUS (monoclonal gammopathy of undetermined significance) in my bone marrow. It can eventually become multiple myeloma, a common bone cancer, but it can also stay at the MGUS stage and not progress. I was seeing an oncologist at this time, as well.

Dr. Schaller, who I'd been seeing and speaking to fairly regularly regarding my Lyme disease, said that many people who are diagnosed with Lyme also have MGUS, and some people can stay there all their lives and never actually develop cancer.

Then, I developed hand tremors. They diagnosed it as Parkinson's, but I think it's neurological Lyme. It started on the right and progressed to the left side. I take Parkinson's medication, but all it really does is take the edge off the tremors. All the neurologists here say "No, you have classic Parkinson's" and don't want to acknowledge the Lyme.

I don't have the brain fog that many people do, thank God. And all my nerve conduction tests came back negative.

My husband is also diagnosed with Parkinson's disease. His is more difficult, I think, because he tested for Lyme in Germany and it came back positive. It was also positive for bartonella and babesia, but we have 29 cats so bartonella is just a part of our life. He never treated his Lyme, though, and I think that's why his so-called Parkinson's has progressed so much worse than mine. He has a lot of balance issues, speech issues, and is starting to have issues with swallowing.

I'm not even going to try to convince the neurologists here or in London of anything. I just gave up on trying to get them to agree that it might be Lyme and we're treating our conditions as best we can with what we have.

How do you navigate having a disease that's largely not recognized where you live?

Most of my friends now understand, fortunately. I've given them things to read and they've checked their own things out, but it's the doctors that make it difficult. My eye doctor, for example, strangely knows what Lyme disease is, but most GPs are in total denial. Some know when you don't expect it, but most still operate under the idea that it doesn't exist.

Some believe in acute Lyme, but believe that two weeks of antibiotics will cure anything. Chronic Lyme doesn't exist in their minds. That makes everything about dealing with this disease difficult.

Take South Africa, for example. It's infested with ticks there. People live outdoors, they run around without shoes and clothes, and so on. Of course Lyme is going to be an issue. But when I was getting diagnosed with Lyme, my sister went and inquired at the university there and they replied that, "No, we don't have any Lyme ticks in Africa."

We even had a friend who was bitten here in Athens, just below our house. I told her to go see Armin Schwarzbach and she was diagnosed with Lyme disease. It's definitely here and people are catching it.

I think that Lyme is everywhere. Well, maybe not in Siberia, you know, but I think that it's virtually everywhere that there are ticks. And it's not just ticks- I'm sure there are also potential risks with other vector animals.

What is your Lyme treatment regimen like today?

Today, I do intravenous IVG, a range of supplements, and herbals. I don't use antibiotics any longer. I'm not sure how successful it is, but I think the IVG keeps me going. I top it up every three weeks. I go and spend a day at the hospital and have the treatment, then go back to my life.

You also have to work with what you can get a hold of over here, or what's available. It's difficult to get stuff shipped in from the States. Customs has started making it more difficult to get anything, so you kind of learn to live with what you can find.

I still have the usual seasonal flares in spring and autumn. It hangs around for about a month in April and May, and then again in October, and then it fades out. The flares usually include joint pain and fatigue, but that's about it. I got used to the cycle and you just kind of live with it, I guess. I've also had COVID twice, so sometimes I'm not sure if it's seasonal Lyme or long COVID.

We live on the beach outside of Athens, so I also swim every day throughout the winter. The water gets cold, as low as 13 degrees Celsius (about 55 Fahrenheit), so sometimes I don't stay longer than five or 10 minutes. However, I think the cold water really helps the inflammation or joint pain. I also try to walk for at least an hour and a half outside each day, and we sea kayak and hike a lot for fun. The outdoors, for me, is the main medicine.

Are you hopeful for the future of Lyme disease?

I think that we're already making progress, and the GLA has contributed to that progress. We just need to make more progress with the doctors, specifically. That's the thing that's missing. We organized a seminar here for Armin Schwarzberg, and he came and spoke. When we published the event, there were only about 15 doctors that were interested.

Funnily enough, one was an infectious disease doctor that I'd been to years before who called and asked me if he could attend. He was one of the ones who told me the symptoms were all in my head and so forth, and that there was no such thing as chronic Lyme. When he called, I said, "So, it sounds like you've changed your mind, eh?"

There's just so much to be learned about Lyme, and I think that it's just so easy for a doctor, after they've studied for so many years, to not want to open another Pandora's box that might cause them to question everything they know. And more importantly, in the case of Lyme, it could cause them to be discriminated against.

But if you look, Germany, Poland, and even Russia are further ahead on Lyme research than Greece. There's definitely been progress since 2005 when I started my journey; in Greece, I'd say it's like 10% better.

How do you think sharing our stories will help others?

I definitely think it will help to hear from someone who's been there. Talking to someone who knows what Lyme is like makes a big difference. We look normal and seem normal, in many cases, but people don't understand that we aren't normal at all. The Lyme disease changes us, and it's harder to accept when you don't know other people who you can relate to.

Do you have any last words of advice or words of encouragement?

Just stay positive. You have to have a sense of humor, which is difficult, but don't take things too seriously. When they tell you it's all in your head, keep insisting because you'll find the right answer eventually. I think it's also just what's available to each person in terms of treatment, and you have to kind of just go with where you live and what's available.

And for me, it's the outside. The fresh air, the sunshine, it's all very healing. Even the cold water from my swims is good. So I would say, get outside.

"Everyday you may not be good,
but there is something good in
everyday"

- Unknown

LYN AMBROSE

St. Ives, Cornwall, England

Independent

Adventurous

Determined

As an immunology and microbiology degree holder, Lyn's story might at first seem like it would be fairly cut-and-dry. However, as we've seen, even those in the medical profession don't always have access to the resources they need to properly diagnose and treat their Lyme disease. What started as an acute tick bite infection that appeared to go away became a decades-long battle for this self-proclaimed "independent, adventurous, and determined" individual.

When and where did your Lyme journey begin?

I got my first Lyme infection in 2007. I was living in Malawi working as a research scientist, and got an acute tick bite. I was at work one day and scratched my head, and a tick fell off - which was good, because I saw the tick, so I was able to relay that to the doctor later. A few weeks later, I was sitting at work again and just came down with uncontrollable shakes. I developed a fever, too.

I went home and didn't return to work for about three weeks. After about five days with a fever, they medically evacuated me from the area. That's what happens when you live in these rural areas. Work had private medical insurance and they had a little plane to fly me out to the capital, which was 700 kilometers away. They were all worried I had a brain infection. The one doctor was worried I had encephalitis, which I did, but they didn't know at the time that it was from the tick.

Fortunately, I went to a local doctor after that and he gave me a very, very good exam and a proper diagnosis of Acute Lyme disease. He called it "tick fever" because they didn't know as much about it at the time, and put me on 10 days of amoxicillin. I was already taking doxycycline as a prophylactic for malaria, which is the first line of treatment for Lyme, so he added the amoxicillin to hopefully improve the outcome and speed of recovery.

He did everything by the book, according to the guidelines. I couldn't have asked for a better experience initially. After a few weeks, I got better and went back to work, and everything was fine.

That is, of course, until about nine years later.

In 2016, I got a job that was less research-intensive but more physically and mentally stressful. The job came with a lot of overwork. I was in charge of three departments that had been neglected, resulting in a 10-year backlog of work. On top of that, I had bosses that weren't doing their part and making my job that much more taxing.

All the pressure and stress built up, naturally. I started sleeping less, getting takeaway on my way home from work, and basically gave up all my good habits. I stopped cycling to work, quit yoga, and so on.

And then, after about six months, the Lyme started coming out.

First, it was a sore shoulder, which I thought was maybe just from too much typing. Then, my hips and glutes were sore and it would hurt even just to sit. It was annoying and painful enough to send me to a chiropractor every couple of weeks, but nothing major that prompted further medical treatment at the time.

Fast-forward to 2018, I was doing much better in my position and I had been given a new boss that was understanding of my situation and the overwork, and I thought now is the time to get my life back. I booked something every night after work so that I would have to leave. I was doing yoga, aerial silk, etc. I just wanted to get back to being really active, thinking that would help.

But, as soon as I did that, I started getting even more sick.

I started having really bad cramps in my calves and my feet were sore. My trainer and I thought at first that it was just because I was using different muscles and tendons doing the climbing and whatnot, but that is a hallmark for bartonella.

Basically, my doctors determined that all the stress from work suppressed my immune system and then the Lyme and bartonella were just woken up because of the suppression. I never knew that they hadn't gone completely with the antibiotics years earlier; I had assumed that the antibiotics worked.

I went to Malawi and read all the books and did all the research. I read all the travel books and tropical health stuff, and plus I have a degree in microbiology- none of that mentioned Lyme. You have sleeping sickness, malaria, TB, etc. I was in charge of the lab at that time and was working with TB and malaria, so I was able to test myself and the tests were all negative.

But there was not a single thing about Lyme, anywhere. So I was lucky that I saw the tick and went to a doctor the first time that knew about Lyme. It was fortunate that the local doctor was so on top of it and familiar with Lyme because years later, in 2018, everything started just one after another. I had joint pain, leg crawling, numbness, absolute fatigue, and so on. I had to just cancel everything with short notice.

What was your journey to getting a diagnosis like?

By the end of 2018, I just couldn't stand up. I had such a heavy head that I was holding it up walking down the street to work. My neck was sore and everything was just hurting all over. Slowly, slowly, I started to remember that I'd had a tick bite back in 2007. I kept going back to my GP complaining about my short-term memory. I actually went three times because I couldn't remember the first two. He'd even tell me that I had been there before and he'd already made the referral. I'd leave feeling embarrassed and a little crazy at times.

Another part of the problem is that I was mostly just ignoring the symptoms. I would feel the crawling sensation and just write it off, or just let the symptoms happen and ignore them as much as possible. I was having horrible stomach issues and diarrhea as much as five times a day. I would just go to the loo, come back to my desk, and go on about my work until the next bout. I was ignoring a lot of what was going on.

I had these weird gut pains that turned out to be kidney stones. Along the way, I saw a gut doctor, a renal doctor, and even ended up back at my GP, just saying listen, something is wrong. I can't remember anything and I've got all this pain and fatigue. And I said, "What I need is a neuro-immuno-endocrinologist. And of course, there's almost no one that does that, so I was told we'd have to see each specialist one at a time.

I started to think, oh no, this is going to take forever.

Six months for this referral. Six months for that referral. Four months for this, three months for that, and so on. I let her do it, of course, because I couldn't do anything. I even went around to all the other GPs at the clinic and eventually they just got annoyed with me.

I knew something was different. I told one doctor that I could feel the inflammation. It's like something was switched on and I refused to let them tell me there wasn't a way to switch it off. This cannot be life. One of the doctors was even like, "You've been good for me before this. Why do you think I'd do this for you when I wouldn't do it for anyone else?"

I was like, well you could have just said you can't order a cytokine panel and told me where I could get one done privately. But, I learned quickly that there are a lot of doctors that aren't going to help you. And if you aren't going to help me, I'm not going to keep asking. I'll go to someone who will help.

One day at work, I just couldn't stand up anymore. I Googled and found a rheumatologist who was across the street, and got an appointment within three days. The reason I chose a rheumatologist was because I'd been seeing a chiropractor for all this pain, every two weeks at this point, and it wasn't helping a ton. One day, I went and everything that he touched just hurt. He said, "Maybe you've got fibromyalgia."

I looked up the information and I read through the information and I could reach 16 or 18 of the points that they referenced, and they were all painful. That's why I chose a rheumatologist, and one that specialized in fibro, no less. I wasn't thinking about Lyme. The rheumatologist gave me three massive steroid injections, and after that I felt amazing. I thought maybe I could just do this a few times a year and it would be good, but that's not how it works. Plus, the steroids can thin the bones after prolonged use, and so forth.

She wouldn't do a lot of tests because I didn't have insurance, so she just did what she could. It was October of 2018 when I got my fibromyalgia diagnosis.

Around the same time, I was realizing that I needed to let my new boss know what was going on. So I went to my (good) boss and he asked, "How are you?"

"I'm sick."

"With what?"

"I don't know."

But my husband and I had been talking and he was like, you've got to let your boss know that something's going on. I agreed, but also didn't really know what to say. So I said, I don't know what is wrong, but something is definitely wrong. My boss sent me to a naturopath, a woman who ran her own health food and vitamin store. She was trained as a pharmacist in Pakistan, but didn't practice here. She was great.

When I finally found my way to her shop, she immediately gave me a stool. Mind you, I'm probably 20 or 30 years younger than her, but she told me, "sit down, you have to sit down."

She wanted me to tell her where it hurt. She asked about my hormones. Tell me this, tell me that. She was really, really good. She knew exactly what she was doing and had very high-quality supplements. She gave me things for inflammation, hormone balance, et cetera. I went back to see her now and then and once she told me that when she first saw me, she had wanted to call somebody because I seemed so sick.

I still hadn't been diagnosed with Lyme disease to this point. That came in 2019.

In February 2019, I was again Googling, trying to find information about fibromyalgia and somehow "Lyme" ended up in my search and I came upon Richard Horowitz's article entitled Are Your Fibromyalgia Symptoms Due to Lyme Disease? on Psychology Today. I was searching, endlessly looking for anything because I just didn't know much about this disease. I couldn't understand it because there was no real information on it. I kept going back to doctors, asking for help, and eventually they met me with an offer of antidepressants because "some people with fibromyalgia have low serotonin."

That, to me, was another situation where, okay, you're not going to help me, fine. I'm not going to ask anymore. So I found myself at Horowitz's article. And I did the screener, which required 46 points to qualify that you might have Lyme, I think, and I got 72. So, I just started thinking, huh, maybe that's what it is. Plus, while I was receiving hyperbaric oxygen therapy in November 2018, even before my Lyme diagnosis, I was constantly seeing signs at the clinic I went to and then I remembered that I had that tick, which led me to search for fibro and Lyme together.

I wanted to go see Jack Lambert, the professor from Ireland that specializes in infectious diseases and Lyme. He had a seven-month waiting list, though, so instead I went to a functional medicine doctor. I have the luxury of working with doctors and scientists all day, so I just asked one of my colleagues if a "neuro-immuno-endocrinologist" was a real thing.

He said, "Well, I do know this guy that works in functional medicine. I studied with him and he's always keen to learn. He might be the right guy for you."

So, I went to him and he did a full workup and said that I scored highly on a lot of areas of the questionnaire, so we'd start with the highest ones and go from there. I got a mitochondrial repair recipe from him that included foods and supplements for mitochondrial repair. I also decided I wanted my own cytokine panel, in addition to the mitochondrial function testing and Lyme testing, just to be sure we covered everything.

When I presented him with my list, he dutifully provided access to the tests I wanted. He also helped me get more information. He was the conduit of putting it all together and getting the testing to get a final diagnosis.

But, when he got my Lyme results, even he didn't know how to interpret it. So that brought its own challenges.

How many doctors did it take for you to get a diagnosis?

I saw a chiropractor, three GPs, four rheumatologists, one renal specialist, and one functional medicine doctor. Oh, and the naturopath my boss recommended. So yeah, nearly a dozen different doctors until my Lyme was officially diagnosed.

How did you feel when you were first diagnosed?

With fibro? I just felt confused. I was really, really confused about this "invisible" illness that I didn't feel like fit. And then, all these doctors tell you that you should "just stop working" because of how sick you are, but it's not that easy. How am I supposed to earn money if I can't work? How can I pay bills? Afford medical treatments?

When I got my Lyme diagnosis, I started Googling again. I searched and searched, and came across TreatLyme.net, Marty Ross's website. He's now my doctor, by the way, and he's great.

I remember I found everything on his site: herbal remedies, supplements, and so forth. I printed the entire 29 pages, highlighted the important things, and thought, "okay, this is it." I did the herbal protocol for about a year based on my research. I couldn't travel to the States to see him, so I had to do with what I had at first.

I think that if I'd had to choose between antibiotics and herbals, I'd have chosen the herbs because my gut was already in bad shape, you know? But then I couldn't find all the herbs because they have different names over here, some of them. Eventually, I found information about their different names and found them, and started a full regimen in July 2019.

What was your Lyme disease treatment journey like?

Well, I mentioned the hyperbaric oxygen therapy in November 2018; I had been Google searching Lyme and fibro and treatment options. I came across a clinical trials program for hyperbaric oxygen therapy in Israel. It said that if you do 40 sessions, three to five times a week intensively, it helps with the pain and fatigue. Obviously, I couldn't travel to Israel, but I found a local clinic to assist.

England has an MS network of centers that do hyperbaric

oxygen therapy for MS patients. They also accept cancer patients, but most don't accept Lyme patients, and the thing is that it's like 15 to 20 pounds there. If you do it privately, it's like 100 pounds, and since I needed 40 sessions, I knew I had to find a better choice. I found one center that accepted anyone with a neurological condition, but it required some travel.

Even though we had no idea what was going on, my boss said I could have six months of adjusted sick leave and no one would ask any questions. I told my boss that I had a plan. I was going to do this therapy, and then I would be good to come back to work (or so I thought at the time).

So during this treatment, I worked two days a week for six months so that I could travel to the center the other three days of the week. It was two trains and a bus to get to the clinic, which took about an hour and a half or two hours one way. On the way back, the train stops at a department store with sofas and beds and all kinds of other home stuff. Sometimes I felt a little like they were going to think I was a homeless person, but I would just stop there for a quick snooze so that I could finish the commute home. Then once I got home, I was on the sofa until bedtime.

After about 10 sessions, my fatigue improved. After 20, my memory improved, so it's definitely helped. The people I met along the way have been so kind, too. The doctors haven't been too helpful, but all of the complementary people I've met have been really kind and generous.

Once I finally had the Lyme diagnosis and started the herbals based on Marty Ross's information, I started to feel a little better. I had also done acupuncture and a lot of other stuff for the pain. I knew from the beginning that I couldn't take pain killers because that would kill my liver. So, I went into a supplement shop and said, "I need something for pain and inflammation." She handed me a giant book, I looked up the options and chose a few, which also seemed to help for the better part of a year.

The tincture that I was taking, I had increased to 20 drops over time, but apparently a little too quickly. It started causing intrusive suicidal thoughts. I wasn't sure it was the supplements at first, but then I discovered it happened when I took the tincture. I reduced the dose and eased back into it, and now everything is okay.

It wasn't until the pandemic in 2020 when Marty opened his clinic online for a short time due to everything closing. I decided to book with him and was lucky enough to get an appointment straight away because he was immediately inundated and closed the clinic. So, I've been seeing him on telemedicine ever since and he's been amazing.

I have been on antibiotics for seven months. I came off them because I was doing well, and then five weeks later, all the symptoms came back. They put me on doxycycline but that gave me a phototoxic reaction that created all this skin pigmentation. Once it started, it kept on for five or six months. For the first few months, I couldn't go out because it was so bad. It didn't cause any pain, but it was distress-ing because my skin was just changing color, bit by bit, and seemed to be getting worse by the day.

I stayed on the herbs, but when everything else came back they put me on clarithromycin and bactrim. I had an allergic reaction to Bactrim, so I had to stop that. Now, I'm taking clarithromycin and fluconazole, which is an antifungal. It doesn't really get rid of the bart (bartonella) but it does help control it. At first, I got confused and was accidentally taking 400mg instead of the 200mg I was supposed to take, but I actually found that it worked better after I'd tried going back to the 200mg.

I still get pains and other symptoms, but the psych stuff I just can't live with. And every time I stop my medication, I get all the mental health stuff right back. I'm irritable, depressed, and if I go three days off the antibiotics, I'm a nutcase. Then I take them again and within 36 hours, I'm back to normal.

How has Lyme disease affected your life?

I remember saying to my staff, "I will make friends with the pain if someone can take the fatigue away."

You can't live with fatigue. You can't do anything.

I'd gone from cycling to work to taking the metro, and even just changing the underground lines was an exhausting walk. I could hardly get to work, and once I got there, I would hide in my office for half an hour or so and just collapse. Then, I'd start working.

There were also many times that I just couldn't leave work. I couldn't bring myself to walk the 10 minutes to the station, so I would stay and keep working, and working, until nine or ten o'clock at night, and then I'd get a cab home. But I couldn't afford that daily expense.

I'm fortunate now that I am fairly functional and I work from home. I could never go back to five days a week in the office. It was fortunate, too, that I was rated in the high-risk category during the pandemic so I've been able to work from home basically since the lockdown started. It's funny,

I said to my dad that I needed a year off just so I could focus on my health. He laughed and said that would never happen, of course. And then the pandemic happened, and I think that's been the single thing that has helped me get better is to have flexible hours and not have to expend the energy going to work.

It also kind of changed my view of the medical community and doctors specifically. My GPs were telling me that it was just wear and tear. My specialist said the issues I was having were due to age, but that wasn't the case. It all came on way too fast and I was far too physically active. I was referred from the first neurologist to a second one because I had done so poorly on the neurological function test. The second neurologist diagnosed me with functional neurological disorder (FND) and said, "There's definitely something interfering with your neurological function. We don't know what it is, but it's something. And it's not Lyme, because Lyme doesn't exist and acute Lyme doesn't do that."

My husband pointed out that what's interesting is he wasn't even curious. None of them were. They were all very matter-of-fact. They were supposed to be the smartest doctors in the world and they didn't care to know more about what I was experiencing or what might be causing it. They just wrote me off and sent me on my way.

In 2018 when things started getting so bad, I was like, well that's my career. This is as high as I'm going to get. I didn't have huge career goals, but I wanted to be able to look around and see where I could go within my field. Then I got so sick and tired that I just didn't care anymore. And now, I'm holding onto my job because I know that if I give it up, I'll never be able to muster the energy to look for another job, go for an interview, etc., let alone start a new job at a new company, learn new people... it's impossible.

I rely now on a lot of systems that I set up in the first few years of being sick and I wouldn't want to have to go through and set that all up again.

Also, just doing stuff. I can't do stuff. And the biggest thing is that I can't plan for what to expect. There's no real planning of anything because I might be fine, but I might not be. I planned to go to Australia and see my parents next month. These are plans we made last year to visit in March. But then two weeks ago I had to cancel the trip because I had a huge flare over the winter months and just went so far downhill that it really wiped me out.

I can't plan tomorrow. I can't plan Saturday or Sunday. I can't plan anything.

One of my therapists said it quite well, she said, "You've lost your relationship with your future."

Am I just going to be sick for 10 or 20 years? Is it always going to be like this? Because I don't want it to be. Am I always going to be spending my income on it? I don't want to. I am earning, but I'm spending just as fast. I can't retire because I can't save.

I have spent 75,000 pounds since 2018. All for doctor's appointments, travel, medications, herbs, therapies and treatments, anything that might offer hope and help for my Lyme. That could have gone into my pension. It could have helped me retire. I don't want to work and just keep throwing my money at Lyme to never get any better.

How has Lyme disease (and having it) impacted you emotionally?

It's very isolating and dark. It's a dark disease. It makes you feel like you're crazy, like you'll never find answers. At the start of 2022, I said to my husband (mind you, things have changed since then), I don't want to be doing this when I'm in my seventies, or even in my sixties. I don't want to look back and see that this is all I did for two or three decades. I am going to give it another two years, I'll give it everything and keep going like I am, but, if it doesn't work, I want assisted dying and I want you to support me in it. Because I'm not going to have you come home and find me having killed myself in the bath or something, I'm not going to do that to you, but I have a right not to live like this.

He didn't like that at all, but I was very firm that you have to be on my side with this.

Then there's the other side of it where you're wondering, am I just going to drop dead one day of Lyme Carditis? I just don't know what the future holds. Should I stay and keep doing this treatment? Should I just enjoy my life because I'm going to drop dead one day? There's a lot of anxiety all around.

You know, none of us know that. I understand we can't tell what's going to happen in the future. But with Lyme, it really just feels so bleak. I'm a lot better than I was, but I still get these things, just small things, but signs that things aren't going right. My nails, for example, they've always been really healthy. But since the Lyme, they've just been getting worse. The nail beds are completely white and they're splitting and catching... It's a little thing, but it's saying that something is not healing.

I thought I had a spider bite on my scalp a few months ago. It was just kind of itchy. But now I've got this thing on both sides of my head and it's itchy, flaky scalp that I've never had before. I think it's an autoimmune thing, but it's still annoying. And while I'm mostly better, I'm also aware there are new pathologies going on. Because I understand microbiology and immunology, I kind of understand what we're up against, so it's been rough.

In the thick of it, Lyme kind of felt like a struggle for the survival of my soul. That's kind of what I think Lyme is.

What has the journey been like with your husband?

I think in the beginning, he was a bit tired of me talking about it. I was so sick and so tired that I kept on talking about it. I was reading all these things trying to figure out what was going on and I was telling him everything and he was like, can we talk about anything else? But then he started to understand. Especially with the lockdown, I think, he got a better sense of how bad it was because he was home with me all the time and saw it more than when he was going out to work each day.

He understands quite a lot about it and he's really support-ive. He can actually pick out the herbs now and sometimes he'll be like, "What did you just take?"

Or, "What are you adding?"

He's been very good from the beginning, too, about taking care of all the things I used to do at home. I would spend my weekends on the sofa barely able to move. He would bring me breakfast and take it away, bring me lunch and take it away, bring me dinner and take it away. I couldn't even put my own plate in the sink. He's been very good about all that.

He's also now been at all of my appointments with Marty since they're online. That helps so that I don't have to remember things or try to repeat everything to him after the appointment, and so forth. I always worried that I would hold him up from being active or doing what he really wanted with his life, but we've managed to work it out and compromise over the past couple years and we actually do really well together.

Like, we're both very active. Once I got Lyme, I couldn't bike like I used to. I had told him at one point that I wanted this fancy designer handbag. He is not a fan of handbags. He thinks they're stupid and spending that much money on one is equally dumb. So, instead, he went out and spent probably five times as much, but he got me a really nice electric bike.

We used to just go biking all day, take bike holidays, and so on. But when I couldn't bike anymore, that stopped. So now I can get back to the outdoors and it's been brilliant for my fitness, freedom, and for us as a couple. We've got a great system worked out. He goes and does his thing and tells me I'm always welcome, but he's quit asking me every time because he knows it makes me feel pressured.

There are some moments when he doesn't get it that I feel so alone, because you can't get it unless you're in it and partially because I'm protecting you from some of it. He does take me to this hill close by. It's a great hill, we just go up there and scream. He even screams with me.

He'll help me get in the bath and wash my hair when I'm going through a flare or struggling with fatigue. He'll bring my favorite food when I can't go out, or treat me to something when he can tell I'm having a rough day.

What has support been like from family and friends?

So far, everyone has been pretty good. I haven't had a single person say "we don't believe you." I think that the most difficult part is that people just don't understand. That's not their fault. Over time, they've come to understand more.

The one thing that has been kind of hurtful is that people don't remember to check in, or they get busy, or what have you. You've got this pretty full-on thing going on pretty much all the time and they just don't bother or remember to see how you are. On the other hand, though, other people have been on top of things. They ask about me, check in regularly, and make sure I have what I need.

I have one good friend who didn't know anything about Lyme, but she's always been there. She's busy too, she's got a job, kids, and so forth. But she's always there to listen, to let me vent, or whatever I need, she saves the space for me. She's basically been like the sister I haven't got.

My family is supportive, they're still in Australia. I was born in Singapore, but since I'm Indian and Chinese mixed, the opportunities weren't great. Indians are treated as second-class citizens in Singapore, which is heavily populated with Chinese people. My parents decided to move us to Australia where we could get an education and have a fair chance in life. From the time I was five, my brother and I grew up in Australia. I left when I was 27, originally just traveling and backpacking around the world. I ended up in the UK because I got seduced by the work. The medical research field right now is very exciting. There are lots of jobs and lots of smart people to learn from, so it's a good time to be here.

Are you hopeful that there is a future for Lyme patients?

I am very heartened by the work that GLA does. I see the money they put into it, the breadth of what they cover, and what they actively do. That creates a lot of hope.

However, I think that it's absolutely criminal that this complex, fascinating disease isn't getting the attention it deserves. It's the most complex genome that we know about and the interplay between coinfections is unique. This should be a big thing in the medical community, but it isn't because of Lyme politics and the stigma attached to Lyme disease.

I think that it's criminal that it's denied as a disease.

That patients are forced to seek self-diagnosis and support groups.

That we have to help each other get drugs and herbs based on where we live in the world.

It makes me really angry, too, that there are all these people with long-term diseases going down a one-way street simply because "it's what happens" when they could probably benefit from long-term antibiotics.

There has to be private money put into this, of course. It's not going to get enough funding from the normal channels. At the same time, too, I think it will come, and maybe in 20 years we'll look back and see how far we've come. But I also have a fear that we'll reach 20 years' time and say "in 20 years' time" again.

I do think the tide is turning, yes. Is it quick enough? I don't know.

How do you feel that sharing your story will help others?

For me, it's cathartic. It's also a way to get recognition out there of an ignored disease that's affecting millions of people around the world.

What is one quote or piece of advice you want to share?

To paraphrase Neil Spector, from one of his books, you're the one who knows the most about you. You've been to all of your appointments. You're the expert on you. Trust yourself.

And I think my advice to Lyme patients would also follow his: do all the things you can to keep yourself as well as possible, because a cure is coming.

Mental Illness
is not a choice

But
Recovery is

NICOLA LAVIN

Galway, Ireland

Resilient

Empathic

Determined

Our next interview comes from Nicola Lavin, a medical scientist from Galway, Ireland. Her story is one that resonates with me because she had so many ups and downs. It took a while to get a diagnosis and she had a son in the meantime, completely changing the experience. Today, Nicola shares her story and life on Instagram and her blog, but it wasn't long ago that she was feeling as bleak as many of those who come across her online presence.

What are three words that you would say describe you?

I think I'm resilient; obviously I think anyone who's been through Lyme has to be resilient. I think I'm empathic, and determined. I just don't let things go.

Is there a song that inspires you?

I have two. The first is from a Scottish band called Belle & Sebastian, called "Nobody's Empire." The lead singer was diagnosed with ME and CFS, so the whole song describes his journey and how isolating it can be. I think it was the first song I'd ever heard from someone who had a similar diagnosis and he described it perfectly. It became a bit of a fight song, I suppose.

The second song is called "Organs" by Of Monsters and Men. Certain lyrics just hit me, like about not giving up the fight and exhausted and trying to survive, and so forth.

Where did your Lyme journey begin?

I was 23, and was heading into my final year of college. I had the summer off beforehand and I wanted to go exploring. So, I headed straight to Montauk in New York and worked there for the entire summer of 2000. I had a great summer enjoying the outdoors, spending time with my college friends, enjoying the wildlife playing around me, it was a good trip.

At the time, I had a long-term boyfriend. He didn't come on the trip, but toward the end of the trip, he came out to visit. He didn't have a working visa so he couldn't stay to work. We ended up going back into the city to Queens where my relatives live and spending time there with them. We would take trips out to Montauk to visit my college friends and go to parties out there. It was on one of those trips that I got bitten by a tick.

I don't actually remember the tick and I don't remember getting bitten, but I had an area under my arm that had gotten really swollen. I didn't get the classic bullseye rash, but it was swollen, red, and looked like a bite. I didn't think much of it, to be honest. I probably should have because I'm a medical science student and I'd learned about Lyme disease and not many people had, but at that time the big thing was West Nile Virus, so like, everyone was just talking about that.

Lyme wasn't considered a big deal, especially in Ireland. It was just a mention in our textbooks from medical school- just a brief explanation of what Lyme is and how it happens, and nothing else. So, naturally, I didn't pay any attention to it. Then, before I came home from that trip, I started to get nauseous and have flu-like symptoms. There was joint pain, too. I was really sick on the plane coming back, but I said I'd wait until I got back to Ireland to see my doctor. I was coming home anyway and they'd probably know me better. So that's what I did. I went to the doctor and she couldn't find anything wrong. I also didn't think to mention the bite at this point.

She told me I had what seemed like a stomach flu and that it should go away in a few days, and not to pay it any attention.

After 10 days, I was still throwing up every day. I was still having joint pain, shivering, and so forth. So I rang her, and because I was so nauseous, primarily, she decided to do a pregnancy test. Lo and behold, I was indeed pregnant.

So, that meant that all of my symptoms were put toward that and nothing else was investigated. The baby was due in mid-June. By February, I had to be hospitalized because I was so sick. They thought it was preeclampsia or something else related to the pregnancy. I was swelling all over, having so many issues, and they had no idea what was going on.

By May, they decided to induce labor and deliver the baby about six weeks early, thinking it would stop all the symptoms I was having. A few days after my son was born, I went into heart failure. I died at one point and they had to revive me. I was in the ICU for two or three weeks on a ventilator. It was a horrific time.

However, once they figured out it was heart failure, they knew it was autoimmune. They had medication to stop it and said the damage done was probably only minimal since they got it under control so fast. But they did tell me that my heart wouldn't be strong enough to have another child. According to them, it was split evenly:

- 33% chance I die
- 33% chance I need a heart transplant
- 33% chance I might make it through with what I have

So, naturally, we crossed more children off the list.

I had been tired before, but after the heart failure I was completely drained. I just could never get my spark or my energy back. I was pushing all the time to get through. And of course, I had a young child and my boyfriend, we'd been together for five years at that point. We were very young when we got together. He decided that he couldn't stick around after that, so I was a single mother doing every-thing by myself, working, and had even gotten my degree in the middle of this.

I wrote up my degree project while I was in coronary care, and not even three months after my baby was born, I was working full-time and dealing with all this heart failure stuff. And it went on like that for years, actually. I would get spontaneous things that would go wrong, like my knees would swell and get inflamed, or I'd end up in A&E with intense pins and needles in my arms and hands. My heart was always really slow, so I was having fainting episodes and what I know now is POTS. I was going to the bathroom 20+ times a night, not getting any good sleep, and all these things were going wrong.

When I went to the doctor, they would just look at the one symptom and not connect the dots. I think it was like nine years like that before I even got my first Lyme test.

At this point, I'm starting to think, like, maybe I got bit by something. Not necessarily a tick, but maybe this is some kind of virus or bacteria I had gotten that was triggering all of these immune reactions. And then when I finally got and took a Lyme test and it came back negative, that was that.

I got the antibody test, and of course after nine years of

battling Lyme you're not going to have those antibodies, so the test wasn't effective, I don't think. But it was the only testing available at the time and with where I was at. Around this same time, I started having issues with my jaw. The dentist originally diagnosed me with TMJ and referred me to an orthodontist. My jaw was locking and shifting, so it was causing serious issues. I had to have surgery to expand my upper jaw to make room for everything to fall back into place. So, I had the surgery and when I woke up from that procedure, all hell broke loose.

I fainted. Then they couldn't stop the bleeding. It was supposed to be a single-day procedure but I had to be in for two days. It was like the final straw that my immune system could take. And around this time, I had just gotten into a relationship. I had been single for seven or eight years, and I had just met a guy right before all this, a really nice guy. He came into my life right about the time I started to get seriously ill.

At this point, the crashes were getting longer and the good days were getting shorter. It was getting to the point where he was carrying me to the bathroom, spoon feeding me, and basically taking care of me entirely. I was having serious esophageal spasms at this time so I couldn't swallow food. I was also having really bad sensitivity to noise and light, which caused paralysis episodes.

I would be stuck, just lying there, all my muscles frozen. I couldn't speak, I couldn't move, I couldn't let my boyfriend or my son know that I was okay. My son would cry and worry about mommy, and of course my boyfriend was worried too. All these neurological symptoms started to come through at this time.

I had heard that Lyme bacteria like to live in the roots of your teeth, and when I had that surgery I think they just kind of shifted and went straight to the nearest organ, which is why I started getting all the neurological symptoms then. I was calling in sick more often than I was making it to work, so I made the decision to take extended sick leave.

I went from making about 80,000 euro per year to nothing. I didn't qualify for a disability allowance or any assistance. No one talks about all the medical bills, but they're not covered by insurance and now you can't work, so how are you supposed to pay them? My husband worked extra, all hours, looking after me and raising our son. Meanwhile, I missed so much of my son's life just living in bed, being bed-bound with Lyme for so long.

What is your relationship like with your son? How has this affected him?

He was scared, I think. He knows that I'm such a strong, determined person. I was hiding a lot of symptoms when he was younger and just pushing through. I had to push through to go to work. To be there for him. To take care of dinner. To be there for others. He would see when I crashed, but when he was younger it was only a week or two at a time. I was traveling with him and doing all the things a parent should and only I knew how tired I was inside.

When it got to the point where I was bed bound and really couldn't do anything any more, it was really scary for him. He was around 11 or 12 years old and I was in bed basically until he was 16 or 17, which was the worst period of my life. And for him, he was having to care for me, worry about me while he's at school, etc.

My now-husband adopted my son and has been so supportive, too. I'm really fortunate that they have that bond and he's been able to step in where I can't. I did what I could with and for my son while I could, and I like to think that he's older now and understands that my lack of presence or ability wasn't anything I could help.

What was your journey to a diagnosis like?

After the jaw surgery, I started to experience really intense head and neck pain that caused me to throw up, have trouble seeing, and so forth. I saw my GP and she sent me for an MRI, which showed that I had two spots of cerebrospinal fluid surrounding my brain and putting pressure on it. They called it idiopathic intracranial hypertension, and referred me to a neurologist.

When I went to see the neurologist, he started to ask about my history and everything else that had been going on. Then, he said to me, "I think you've got Lyme disease."

He was the first doctor that really showed any interest or that wasn't dismissive because I had a negative Lyme test in my records. He said he was going to treat me like an MS patient and kind of put me on their treatment program to see if it helped or not.

He was going to bring me into hospital for a week and put me on a strong course of steroids to help pull me out of my big crash so that I could regain some sort of life again. Unfortunately, that week of steroids caused me to react in such a bad way. They couldn't figure out what was happening, either. When he came around again, he said, "I really think you have Lyme. If you give Lyme patients too many steroids, it suppresses their immune system and you don't need that anymore suppressed than it already is."

He suggested that I get my labs done in Germany because no one in Ireland was doing proper tests. I sent my blood-work to Germany and also requested a PCR test. When I got the result of a positive Lyme test, I actually celebrated because I knew what it was. I had a glass of champagne with my sister. I was like, "I know what it is now!"

At this point, I'd started to question my own sanity. There's so much gaslighting and victim-blaming that it's hard. At the end of the day, I started asking, could I be making myself sick? Even though I knew that went against my personality and who I am, I had to question it for a minute. So once I got the positive test, I felt validated.

But then, the battle began. I now had to get the doctors in Ireland to even recognize the results.

What was your official diagnosis?

My test came back positive for the PCR and the Lyme, as well as borrelia burgdorferi, rickettsia, and chlamydia pneumonia.

What was your treatment journey like?

The neurologist did help me. He brought me in for three months of IV antibiotics. I feel like they might have helped some, but by this point I felt like I had killed off so much of the bacteria but there was so much damage that needed to be repaired. I also found an infectious disease consultant in Dublin who is treating patients now, and I did two years of oral antibiotics.

While I do feel like it helped and probably got rid of the Lyme, it also killed off my gut microbiome and immune system, which led me back to Germany for other treatments. I had researched and found a program they were doing at the time with stem cells. Unfortunately, the clinic I went to is no longer operating, but I had one treatment and it was quite successful. It was a long process, and it was nearly worse than when I was really sick with the Lyme in the first place. But my good days were getting longer and my bad days were getting more sparse.

I was finally able to travel. For so long, I wasn't able to be independent of him because he did all of the physical things and made sure I was taken care of. Once I finished my stem cell treatment, I started traveling. My blog was noticed by this travel group in India while this was going on, and they invited me over for this magical, once-in-a-lifetime trip with like, 30 other bloggers. India just feels like such a healing place; I'm not sure why. This was a huge moment because I was independent and on my own, in a completely different country.

I'd gone from bed-bound and hopeless to dancing around a bonfire in India.

How many doctors did you see before you were diagnosed?

By the time I got my official Lyme diagnosis, I had seen 22 doctors, including GPs, specialists, and any number of other medical professionals who claimed to be able to help.

What advice do you have for others in the Lyme community?

Just appreciate the everyday. You don't know where life is going to take you and you don't know when the opportunity will be taken away from you, so go and do it and appreciate it now.

How are you doing today?

I will never be at 100% again, but I can live at like 80 to 90%, so I'm happy. Last year, I started to develop gyneco-logical problems. I had fibroids and heavy bleeding, which eventually led to me becoming anemic. I ended up in A&E and they wanted to do a chest x-ray for whatever reason. Luckily, they did, because they found a tumor on my ribs. I had bone cancer and had to have two ribs removed.

But the way I was treated with that was so completely different from Lyme. People just don't understand how bad Lyme disease can be. I got more sympathy for saying I have bone cancer than, you know, saying I've lost a decade of my life to Lyme disease. Losing your quality of life is one of the worst things you can ever experience.

I hate to ask, but which would you have chosen?

Definitely the bone cancer. It sounds terrible, but even though it was scary and I felt like I had had more than my share of medical issues, there's a treatment protocol. There are boxes to check and a plan can be made and you can do things about it. The way I was treated, too, was night and day. With Lyme, people dismiss you, make you feel like you're exaggerating, tell you Lyme doesn't exist, and so forth.

Friends, relatives, colleagues, everyone treated it so differently. With the Lyme, there's no treatment protocol. There's no standard. There is no awareness. No guidelines. People treat it like it's not a life-threatening illness. It's fine if it takes longer to diagnose and treat or if it goes undiagnosed. That's hardly the case, though. People don't talk about Lyme Carditis, neurological Lyme, and other potentially dangerous symptoms. And if nothing else, you're watching life from the sidelines. It may not be life-threatening, but it is absolutely life-altering.

What kind of impact has Lyme disease had on your life and other relationships?

Well, I missed out on my late 20s, my 30s, and plenty of work options, travel plans, and so forth. Plus, it's just such a scary place to be. Without my husband, I couldn't have supported myself and my son. Friends disappear. They try to be there but I suppose when you're never going to get any better they just fade out. You're constantly complaining, missing birthdays and other events, and struggling to just exist. They disappear, just stop calling, and you end up left on your own.

I've always considered myself close to my sisters. My mom was my biggest supporter, but unfortunately, she had a heart attack at my sister's wedding and passed away. So initially, that support was gone, but I've been working to find it in other places.

What do you hope to gain by sharing your story?

What I find now from sharing my story on Instagram and online is that people will sort of think that you're looking for attention when that's not the case at all. I find that a little difficult to deal with because I don't share my story for myself. I share it for those who are coming behind me. Those who are just getting diagnosed. Those who are having a whole host of symptoms that they might not know what they are. I share to let people know there is hope, and that you can get better from this.

Your story can be somebody else's survival guide. I think it's just important to share and raise empathy for all those chronic illnesses where you look fine on the outside but you're dying on the inside. That just because you look okay doesn't mean that you are okay. I think it's really important to put a voice to that and make people aware that chronic illnesses are a thing and people do struggle with them. Quality of life is so important, and I think we often overlook that.

Do you have hope for a cure for Lyme disease?

Well, there's a few parts to this. First, I don't think it's ever going to be one cure that fixes every situation. I also think it's not the cause that we need to figure out, but what actually happens in your body once you get Lyme disease that keeps it in that cycle of symptoms that seems to never end. If we can figure that out, we might get some answers.

I feel like, right now, it's very much like the more money that you have, the more you can put into your treatment and the more options you have. The people who are allowed to or who can afford the time to recover are doing better than those who are having to battle it everyday, continue working, etc. I do feel like eventually, the gut microbiome will come into it at some point. And while I do think that might make people a little more sympathetic, I don't think they'll ever fully understand.

What has your path to recovery been like?

I think I've tried everything. I did the herbs, the antibiotics, I supported with supplements, I changed my diet, tried tons of different types of diets, I would've tried anything, honestly. What works for one person doesn't work for another, which is the bit that's hard, I find. There's no specific "do this and you will feel better" with Lyme disease like there is with other illnesses.

The week or two after stem cells, I felt immediately better because of all the therapies, including that one. However, I did start to develop other symptoms. I had a lot of histamine, so it created this kind of anxiety that I couldn't really shake until the histamine levels were reduced. It was like two years of recovering until I felt completely better. However, in that two-year period, I was getting longer and longer periods of good days. And within three months of the stem cell treatment, I was heading off (without my husband) on my trip to India.

Personally, I find that eating mostly plant-based and trying to work on my gut microbiome helps. And of course, the stem cells had a good impact for me.

What did you do to distract yourself during all this?

The hypersensitivity made it hard to watch TV or listen to music, which made it even more isolating because I really, really like music. On the days I was feeling better, I went to Instagram. I know it sounds petty to say, "Oh, Instagram is great!" or whatever, but I wanted to see people traveling. I used Instagram to give myself hope and live vicariously, hoping that maybe someday it could be me.

My husband was great, too. He would try to get me out of my head and focus on things like, "One day, we're going to do this" or "Someday, we'll go there" and give me the hope and belief that got me through to the next day.

What do you do today?

Today, I still meditate, take time to ground myself and focus on living in the moment. I try not to let life's pressures overwhelm me. I still do the plant-based diet and try to exercise when I can but I've never been able to do much more than walk because it triggers crashes. I do walk, when I can, but I'm nearly afraid to push it any further. If anything, I'm more mindful of my body and its limits, and more respectful of them.

Do you have any words of encouragement or advice?

There's a quote I've always said that I like to share:

We fall, we break, we fail, but then we rise, we heal, we overcome.

And I feel like even after you've healed, you have a lot to overcome. Your brain has to process everything you've been through, and with Lyme, you're constantly fighting what feels like an uphill battle. However, you will get there, if you just keep pushing along. And hopefully for those who come behind me, you will get there more quickly.

HARISH ANDELA

Hyderabad, India

Creative

Independent

Determined

Harish Andela is a self-described creative, independent individual from Hyderabad, India. He was one of many who contracted Lyme at a young age, but didn't know much about it at the time. He started thinking that his lack of energy and motivation were simply part of his constitution, not related to a medical issue, but over time, the signs became more obvious that something was seriously wrong.

What three words would you say describe you?

Before Lyme I might have had a better answer, I guess… but for now I'd say creative, independent, and determined.

Do you have a song that inspires you?

I like Red Hot Chili Peppers. "Under the Bridge" is the one I've been listening to on repeat lately, but I like "Scar Tissue" and all the others too. One song that is an all-time favorite is "A Horse with No Name" - I'm not sure who the band is.

How did your Lyme journey begin?

I probably contracted Lyme at a very young age, like eight or 10 years old. I used to live at my aunt's place and they had a dog. I remember that I got bit by a tick that was on the dog, but at the time I didn't think anything of it because I was so young. However, immediately after that, I developed a red meat allergy. I went to the doctor and they gave me some medicine and said that I'd better stop eating meat for a while.

Fortunately, most of my diet is vegetarian so giving up meat wasn't a big deal. I stopped eating meat for six years or so, to no avail. I used to always feel sick, fatigued, tired - I had less energy than classmates, but thought it was just my constitution that I was like this. Maybe I was just a low-energy person.

Then, I went to college and I started having these terrible headaches. It's somewhat more hectic than high school, so I thought maybe that played a part, as well as with the lack of energy. However, the general malaise, lack of energy, lack of appetite, and so on all continued throughout college and eventually I figured maybe there is something actually wrong with me. At the time in India, the Internet wasn't readily available on mobile devices or elsewhere. You either had a computer at home that was connected to the Internet or you went to an Internet cafe to pay to use a computer for a specific period of time. So, there was limited access to research and resources.

I started going to all these doctors, explaining my head-aches, the tiredness, lack of appetite, and other symptoms. I'd tell them how I'd wake up in the morning feeling like I haven't slept when I had, in fact, slept for eight or 10 hours the night before. They did a lot of tests and scans and referred me to other doctors.

I think I went to like 10 or 15 doctors in total, and finally they came to the conclusion that I was either just stressed or depressed (or both). All the tests they did were negative. There was nothing to explain the symptoms; especially since I had these unexplainable symptoms like headaches, which could be attributed to stress, and the same with fatigue, and so forth.

So since all the tests came back fine, they said to my parents, "He's probably either stressed or depressed. You should consider psychiatric, because there's nothing that we can do for him. We have done all the tests we can think of and he's been to enough doctors that if there was something medically wrong, we would have found it by now.

So I told my parents, fine, let's go to the psychiatrist. But right away, even when I was talking to the psychiatrist, I could tell that I wasn't just stressed and depressed. I was depressed because I was sick and I told them that. Their response, of course, was that many people don't realize they are depressed until they start treatment. Once the treatment works, they start feeling better and realize that they were wrong. So, I started on SSRIs as well as other psychiatric medications to help with the fatigue. I used to sleep pretty much all day long. Even now, I'm tired most of the day, but it was much worse back then.

I took the medications. I went to my appointments. And nothing was changing. If it is depression, I should be feeling better, right?

Well, the psychiatrist said not necessarily. He said that sometimes different medicines don't work for some patients so we have to keep trying different ones to find what works for you. I was on a rotation of different medications for a long time, and I was also attending counseling sessions. At every session, I'd go and sit in the waiting room, waiting my turn to be called and I'd think to myself:

'This isn't working at all. This isn't what's wrong.'

The counselor used to ask me how I was feeling, what my dreams are, things like that, and I had no complaints or issues in that regard. I kept thinking that the issues aren't in my personal life or social life. The only problems are these symptoms that won't go away and that no one can diagnose. He had good intentions, but it was no good to me because I had Lyme, not a psychiatric condition.

Lyme, by the way, isn't really a thing in India. Until now, I've only been in touch with three different Lyme patients from India and only one of them got infected here. The others got infected in the U.S. or Australia. So I think it's not as prevalent here as in other countries. It's not a diagnosis that doctors are aware of. It doesn't occur to them that Lyme disease may be present because they aren't even taught about it.

I eventually stopped the psychiatry because it wasn't helping, obviously. I was with him for just over a year and it didn't do any good. I was going to graduate college, which gave me regular access to the Internet for the first time in my life. Once my courses were done, I used that access to search for symptoms, conditions, and anything I could find to try to make sense of what I was dealing with. At that time, the only information I found was on fibromyalgia and chronic fatigue syndrome (CFS).

Another reason that I didn't think it was Lyme disease (or could be) is that I'd been to a doctor previously, a rheuma-tologist, and he mentioned that my symptoms could be explained by Lyme, but since I hadn't been outside of India, we could rule that out. So, I didn't even consider Lyme after that point because that doctor told me it couldn't be the case- I don't remember his exact words, but it was defi-nitely insinuated that since I hadn't traveled outside the country, it could be ruled out.

I thought, 'Okay, so I have CFS. What do I do now?'

I went to a couple of doctors and asked them what I could do, or what I should do. Many of them consider CFS to be a mental issue, not a physical ailment. They think it's psychological and the only way you get help is by seeing a psychiatrist or making behavioral changes, etc. I knew immediately this wasn't going to help me. They suggested I go to a better psychiatrist and maybe I'd get a better outcome.

So, I tried a second psychiatrist. I only saw this one for three or four months. I had no confidence that it would even work from the beginning, and the experience was the same as with the first psychiatrist. So, after four months, I was done. I wasn't going to keep wasting money on something that wasn't working. I continued to try to find someone who knew what to do about chronic fatigue, but there was no one.

At this point, I had visited like 30 or 40 doctors and they all said it's psychosomatic or psychiatric.

"You should be under long-term psychiatric care. You're wasting your time and money on all these specialists looking for different answers."

I'm exhausted by all of this and now frustrated with the lack of what medicine had to offer, so I thought about alternative treatments. I went to a few different homeopaths over the course of two or three years, but that didn't help at all, either. We still didn't know it was Lyme causing the issues in the first place, so it was a trial-and-error process of trying to find supplements to alleviate the symptoms.

I did feel some small changes, but any noticeable changes were usually negative. I had officially run out of options with Western medicine and alternative therapies. Even yoga and exercise weren't helping- they help mentally, but not physically in regard to the Lyme symptoms.

What was your journey to getting diagnosed?

So from the time I was 10 years old and developed the meat allergy until I got a diagnosis was a good decade of my life. I had pretty much given up on figuring out exactly what was wrong with me after seeing so many doctors and not getting answers. I was stuck with CFS, but now what? You can't get an official diagnosis from a doctor here in India for CFS. And even then, how do you treat it?

They'd just send me back to psychiatry, so it was discouraging. I was reading all of these research articles and trying to find something tangible that could help. Maybe I could find a treatment, a better diagnostic tool, et cetera, et cetera.

That led me to a place here in India that works with rare diseases. They aren't doctors, but a group of volunteers who work with people who have rare diseases of all kinds. I figured I would go to them and explain my situation and my history, and then ask them directly if they have any better guesses because I've run out of options. Any insight, guidance, or support I could gain would be helpful.

I talked to the founder, who lives in the U.S. half the time and in India the other half, and his first question was, "Did you get tested for Lyme disease?"

I told him that I remembered a doctor bringing it up a long time ago, but since I hadn't been outside of India, it can't possibly be Lyme disease, so I was told that I didn't need to worry about getting tested. The founder told me that I need to get tested, so I went to a local rheumatologist and said, "I have all the symptoms and was asked by another person to specifically get tested for Lyme disease. I'd like to do the test, even if you might think it's not a possibility."

The rheumatologist said that we would prescribe a test to the laboratory. So I got an Eliza test, which I think is one of the more unreliable testing options, and the results came back inconclusive. It wasn't negative for Lyme, but it wasn't positive, either.

But for me, for the first time, everything made sense. I remember having the tick and it being embedded in my scalp for so long and being so hard to pull out because of how long it was in there. I also remember developing the meat allergy around that same time, which I read was another similarity I shared with Lyme patients. And many of the other symptoms started about that time, too.

It made far more sense than CFS, so I started looking for better tests and better doctors that know about Lyme disease in India. I found one doctor in Delhi, our capital, and she has a history of treating Lyme patients from Europe and America with stem cell therapy. I found her name in an article about another patient who wrote a book about her Lyme disease and said that this doctor is the one that helped her get better.

So, I called the clinic and told them I'd heard about their treatments for Lyme and that I wanted to come get diagnosed and treated, if it is Lyme. She told me to come to the clinic and we would do the test, but at the time the stem cell therapy was on hold. After talking to her, I learned that the Indian Medical Association was investigating her for an accusation of using unproven treatments on patients. She had been treating Lyme, neurological disorders, people who had lost limb function, etc. And she had varying degrees of success with all of them, including using stem cell therapy to treat Lyme patients.

Because she was under review, she couldn't use stem cell therapy until the case was finalized. So, she told me that they could at least test and find out what's going on. She said they would see if it is Lyme and then try antibiotic therapy, too. So she sent my sample to IGeneX in California and she also did a spect scan of my brain. Naturally, I got the spect scan results well before the test results came back.

She looked at the scan and told me that even though the Lyme test was still out, my brain scan showed indications that have been seen in other Lyme patients. So, although it's a preliminary diagnosis, let's wait until we get the test results. I don't remember exactly, but I think it took two or four weeks for the results to come back from the U.S. I got a call from the doctor and she told me that it was indeed Lyme disease and that I should come to Delhi to discuss the treatment protocol.

And then, the pandemic happened.

In addition to the trial that she was dealing with, she also said that we should wait until the COVID pandemic died down to start treatment. So, I had to wait, all this extra time, without knowing whether the treatment would even help or not. I was so eager to get treated that I used to wake up every single day hoping for a vaccine or a change in the status of the COVID outbreak. This was the first diagnosis that made sense and it's the first real treatment I'm doing that doesn't involve not knowing what I'm treating.

I was fortunate that I got her to agree to let me come before the vaccine was released because I told her I would take all the necessary precautions and so forth. I think I was just persistent and so she decided to go ahead.

Of course, then I started thinking about, what if this treatment doesn't work? I was already in a bad headspace because even though I finally had a diagnosis, I kept reading all these horror stories online of patients who don't get better for years and years. I couldn't come up with any good answers and was only drawing bad conclusions, so I went back to relying on the hope that it would work.

I was put on oral and IV antibiotics for two weeks. Then, the rest of the protocol was oral antibiotics so she told me I could return home and she would check-in and prescribe them over the phone. As I suspected, they didn't work. I had a slight improvement in the very beginning, but it was very slight and didn't result in any significant benefits. I called her to ask what else we could do.

She advised me that oral antibiotics can only do so much, which is why she started working with stem cell therapy. But since that's on hold, she was kind of at a loss. She didn't say as much, but I kind of got the feeling of, "Well, I don't really know how else to help you."

I felt like I was stuck between a rock and a hard place.

There aren't a lot of ways that you can visit the U.S. or other countries from India. You can get a tourist visa, but that's only good for a couple of months, which isn't helpful if you need extended treatment. It's also very expensive to travel to the U.S. because of the exchange rate, so it's not something that is easy to do.

At this point, I couldn't hold a job for long because I was so sick and exhausted all the time. And all the jobs that I could hold didn't pay nearly well enough for me to travel to the U.S. to get the treatment I needed.

Finally, I found an American doctor. I discovered her through another Lyme patient that I met on Facebook. She had been documenting her care and really liked her doctor, so I asked if she could get me a referral. So, I'm currently seeing her, but it's frustrating because it's still not a linear path. There are no clear answers.

What is your current treatment regimen?

Currently, I am on antibiotics and some herbal supplements. I have seen some improvements, but they have been very slow. I was on one antibiotic for too long and it affected my gut microbiome so I had to start another antibiotic and it's not working as well. We're trying to figure out different options that could work, as well. So far, though, we haven't found any yet.

I didn't see a significant difference from the herbals alone, but I still take them with the antibiotics and some probiotics for gut health.

How are your symptoms today?

They have their ups and downs. Some days are better, some are worse.

How has this impacted your life?

In high school, I was ambitious and studious. I figured I'd go somewhere in my life. But being ambitious and having Lyme is not a good combination. It's not good for your mind because you want to do all of these things that Lyme doesn't allow you to do, so I had to disappoint myself and my parents, and I guess probably my friends, too.

I struggled with tempering my ambitions when I saw my friends doing things. It's hard to talk to my friends because they have decent jobs and lives and stuff. And when they call me and we do talk, it's different. It's hard to maintain friendships. It impacts your social life in many different ways.

I used to hope and pray for a diagnosis, even if it was a bad one, just because I wanted answers. And now that I have the Lyme diagnosis, I don't know. I feel like even though I know the answer, I haven't been able to do anything about it, so it's hard.

I guess I'm just disappointed that the answer I have isn't what I wanted or expected.

It's also hard because I don't have a lot of people to relate to here in India. If I lived in the U.S. or somewhere with more connections, I guess maybe it wouldn't be so lonely. I am friends with a couple of Lyme patients in the U.S., but it's hard to keep in touch because of the distance and the time difference and so forth. I have two friends here in India, but they live in different cities and have their own lives and things to worry about, so again, it's often hard to keep in touch.

What are your family relationships like?

They're not good, because it's hard to explain to them that the doctors are wrong. Lyme patients have to deal with families not recognizing their illness or symptoms, I guess, but here I'm basically the only one. They don't want to fight so they don't mention it. We just don't talk about my illness.

I don't give my parents too many details because I feel like when I tell them about things and then it doesn't work, I get disappointed and they're doubly disappointed, and it also kind of reinforces that idea of, "He's just making this all up."

You say you had this disease, and that you got treated for it, so why aren't you any better?

So, I kind of stopped talking about it. The same thing with my sister. It's hard to talk about.

Do you have a current support system?

I have a friend who has CFS and she is the only one I discuss my illness with because she faces a lot of the same difficulties in her own life. I have other friends from college and school, but it's hard to talk to them about what's going on, what Lyme is, and so forth.

It's very isolating and living in India makes it even harder to connect with others since the condition isn't known, recognized, or understood well here.

Where are you on your path to recovery?

I think I am very much still in the beginning of the journey. It's hard to assess because I haven't even found something that works yet. I'm in a group called Generation Lyme, they do Zoom meetings with people from all over the world. All of the stories are so wildly different. Some people get better quickly and others have tried everything and still aren't better. It's hard to assess where I am on my journey because I don't know.

What is your daily routine like? What do you do to help your Lyme?

Meditation helps, and having a flexible work schedule helps, too. I'm a freelance copywriter. The pay isn't great, but I can basically make my own schedule, so that's helpful. I'm a hypersomniac. I need like 10 hours of sleep a night to feel like a human being the next day. It's interesting because a lot of Lyme patients I talk to are insomniacs or struggle with sleep, and I need as much of it as I can get.

What do you think about the future of Lyme patients? Are you hopeful for a cure?

Well, honestly, even though the long COVID thing is bad, obviously, I feel like it's been a huge help for CFS, Lyme, and other chronic illnesses. It brought to light the suffering of patients that people otherwise didn't know about. I think that now there will be more research and I hope that it will benefit everyone with chronic conditions, and that could translate into future solutions for Lyme and other diseases.

NICOLE JONES

Alberta, Canada

Creative

Driven

Positive

The next story in our journey comes from Nicole, who is a creative, driven individual from Calgary, Alberta, Canada. What started out as a "weird spider bite" quickly became much more. Living so far away from most major medical providers also made it difficult to find answers and drove up the costs associated with finding and obtaining the best treatment. Let's hear Nicole's side of things.

What are three words that describe you?

I would say creative, driven, and positive. It was really hard to decide.

Is there a song that inspired you or helped you through your journey?

String Lights by Peter McPoland; all of his music, honestly, is so good.

When did your Lyme journey begin? At what age did you see symptoms, etc.?

I think I got bit when I was 13, but I'm just assuming. It was the summer of 2012 and I was helping lay sod for a soccer field. I noticed this bite and didn't think much of it at first. I remember on the drive home, I started to get cold sweats and I remember thinking that it must be from the bug bite. Then, I started to worry that it might be something serious. However, by the time we got home, it was fine and I forgot about it for close to a year.

Then, I started to develop flu-like symptoms. I remember being really cold all the time. I would take three baths a day sometimes just to warm up. I also started having some serious stomach problems and was trying a variety of food-elimination diets to assist with those. I was still figure skating and my knees also started to bother me during this time. I was seeing doctors for that, as well as physiotherapists, my family doctor, and others. It was just all these random little things that seemed unrelated and they just thought I was really unlucky that all this stuff was happening.

I was bloated pretty much 24/7 and started having trouble with nausea and issues with my appetite. I had aches and pains, too. It felt like every month or so there would be a new thing and then another new thing, and so on. It was never-ending. And since we lived so far north, there weren't many specialists in the area. So anytime we were referred to a specialist, we were driving between two and six hours to each appointment.

That made these disappointing appointments even more frustrating because of how far we had to travel. Fortunately, my mom was taking me to all of my appointments and she was a huge help throughout the entire thing. I don't think I'd have gotten diagnosed without her. She helped me advocate for myself with the doctors when they would suggest that I was making it up or that it was somehow in my head.

It did take a little to convince her in the beginning, you know, just because I was fatigued and feeling generally terrible, which is hard to explain. She thought maybe I was just becoming a teenager and going through all those changes, but I finally convinced her that no, I just feel like trash all the time.

So, I started to get x-rays, ultrasounds, blood work, all of the tests- everything was starting to add up. But, every-thing came back normal. I was a "picture of perfect health" and they couldn't help because there was nothing wrong with me.

Multiple doctors asked if I'd tried taking Advil, as if that was somehow the magical solution to all this pain and discomfort. Then, they decided that I must just have a low pain tolerance and it was just everyday aches and pains that I was interpreting as this intense pain.

First of all, what teenager has "everyday aches and pains" anyway?

But, we pressed on. We thought I had Lupus because that's prevalent in my family. Both of my mom's parents have it. So, based on my family history we assumed maybe that would be it, but the blood work never showed any autoimmune factors. We were also trying to catch inflammation that we thought must have been there, somewhere.

I would actually save my blood work referral until I felt the absolute worst, and then I would go get it done, hoping that maybe since I was having a really bad day, something would finally show up. But it never did.

I saw rheumatologists, gastroenterologists, all the specialists. And nothing.

Eventually, the discs in my jaw both slipped out of place, just on their own. I woke up one morning and couldn't open my mouth because the bone was hitting the disc and it couldn't open. Then, it shredded the disc so that it could open. I was about to get my wisdom teeth out and the surgeon thought it would help, for some reason. When they did the x-rays for that, though, they could see that there was something wrong with the joint. They weren't sure what, but they could tell it wasn't right.

Of course, the wisdom teeth removal didn't help so we looked into it more. They did a bone scan on my jaw and realized I would need surgery. I ended up getting open-joint jaw surgery on both sides. They made new discs out of skin from my leg.

And even then, the doctors were like, "This is from an injury?"

"Nope."

"High-impact sports?"

"Nope."

"I literally just woke up like this one morning."

I remember at one point we were eating soup and I was in so much pain that I was sweating so much, and I couldn't sit still because moving my mouth at all was so incredibly painful.

So, when they did the surgery, they didn't wire my jaw shut or anything. It was super swollen; I was on a diet of mostly liquids for a long time. Slowly, it got back to normal, and did some physio exercises to restore motion. It's pretty much good now— I can't chew gum or tough things really, but it doesn't really affect me anymore. Sometimes when I yawn it's painful, but not regular pain on a daily basis or anything.

I reacted really badly to the antibiotics they gave me after my jaw surgery. I had a full body rash, my face was red and inflamed and textured, and my skin burned, all over my body. It was a couple of weeks after I had finished the antibiotics, though, so they thought it might be something else. It slowly went away, but took months and months for my cheeks to go back to normal.

Even though these visible things were starting to happen, they were still telling me that whatever I had was psychosomatic and I should see a psychiatrist and be put on anti-anxiety medication. I really thought that after the jaw and the rash and everything that they could see, they would finally believe me.

Finally, they're going to believe me!

Nope.

I did see a psychiatrist, just once. It was very strange. He was really dismissive, even though his job was dealing with all this "not physical stuff". We were talking and he cut me off and was like:

"So do you want me to medicate you or not?"

How was I supposed to respond? I don't know why I'm here, how am I supposed to know if I need medicine? Isn't that your job? Of course I have anxiety because I can't go to school and I can't do anything and everyone's telling me that I'm crazy. Of course it's going to affect my mental health... It was frustrating because they thought it was because of my mental health, not the other way around.

At this point, I probably hit my lowest point and started to kind of believe that I was just making it up, and that stuck with me. I struggle with it even now. I have to ask my boyfriend sometimes, like, did that even happen to me?

It's just like, especially at such an impressionable age, being told by a doctor, a person of power who's supposed to know about health, that you're lying and there's nothing wrong with you and you must be making it up for attention—that's really impactful and disheartening. And at this point, I'd been going through this for a couple of years.

So, I still have a hard time believing myself and remembering everything because of that. I think that's one of the most important things for Lyme patients:

To have someone believe them.

What was your journey to a diagnosis like?

Well, I grew up in a small town and the pharmacist in our town had a son that was going through Lyme treatment, interestingly enough. I was always bringing my prescriptions to get them filled and he would talk to my mom about stuff. He was basically seeing my symptoms through my medications and the gears were turning in his head and eventually, he pulled my mom aside and said, "I think you should look into Lyme disease."

He told her about how she needed to find a Lyme-literate doctor and that the medical system won't help us any further. She came home and told me about that, and I immediately Googled Lyme disease. When I saw the pictures of the rash, I thought back to that spider bite and I remember that I got a little excited because, like, finally we might have an answer.

Plus, I had seen that the CDC said two weeks of antibiotics usually takes care of it, so that didn't sound too bad. The pharmacist warned my mom that it wasn't that easy, though. He suggested that I see a naturopathic doctor that's about an hour away. So, we made an appointment and went to see her.

My appointment with her was crazy. She believed everything. She listened to me, asked questions that no one had before, and was very thorough in discussing things and addressing my concerns. I remember smiling ear to ear the entire time. And she agreed that I needed to be tested for Lyme, so we got my blood sent to IGeneX in California.

Unfortunately, the test came back as a debatable positive. It was positive for babesiosis, and bordering on positive for Lyme. The naturopath explained that babesiosis doesn't really cause symptoms on its own; it needs to be with Lyme disease to do that. So she decided to go ahead and give me a clinical diagnosis of Lyme disease even though the test wasn't a clear positive.

I was really, really happy at this point. I think I almost started tearing up. She was like, "Okay, I know this sounds exciting, but this is going to be a long process. It's not just an easy two weeks of antibiotics. It could take some time."

But I didn't care, because someone was finally listening and not telling me I was crazy or making things up.

This was in 2017, about five years after the initial bite.

What did the treatment journey look like?

Well, in Alberta, there's a law that doesn't allow naturo-pathic doctors to prescribe medicine, so she was working through a prescribing pharmacist for a little bit, but then he got flagged and had to stop. So I got treatment through her naturally for a while, but wasn't finding much im-provement with supplements alone. I think she got a little frustrated with me because I was such a difficult case.

Eventually, I started to see a naturopathic doctor in British Columbia, which is a nearby province. In BC, they're allowed to prescribe. We did phone appointments because she was located in Vancouver, a few days' drive from where

I live. There was a long time of trying to get something prescribed to me, and when I started seeing her, we started mold detoxing and testing for mold, which also ended up being a big turning point in my treatment.

I did take doxycycline, but it made me extremely nauseous. I couldn't keep it down, so I had to stop that. Eventually, I decided to take a trip to Vancouver to do some hyper-thermic treatment. That essentially brings your body up to a high fever range, and they keep you there for like four hours, forcing your immune system to engage. The naturo-path suggested this because most people with Lyme have dormant immune systems.

Since I was in Vancouver, I also did IV antibiotics for about a month. But then we had to stop the heat treatments because my heart was starting to do strange things. And that's when I started to figure out how the Lyme was affecting my heart. Anytime they heated up my body, my heart rate would speed up. And when it does that, it skips a lot of beats, so it gets really dangerous.

My naturopathic doctor was listening to my heart and said it sounded like a horse tripping. We found out I had PVCs (premature ventricular contractions). That's when we started to get into the heart journey. After that, I would get really bad chest pain, really dizzy, clammy, chest pain radiating down my arm, just a gross feeling in my body. While I was in Vancouver I had to go to the ER because of my heart. One night I had chest pains so bad I couldn't take it, so I went to the ER and they did blood work and an ECG and the doctor described it that I was "so healthy my heart was beating too hard."

When I told that to my naturopath, she got the blood work they ordered. She said my potassium was so low that I could have had a heart attack at that time, but it seems like they didn't even look at the test results. They just sent me home. She (my naturopath) prescribed potassium immediately. She thought maybe because of the heat treatment, my body was just sweating out too much for some reason. But, she also told me I should get a full cardiac workup when I get back to Alberta, just to be safe.

So, I called to make an appointment and asked for a cardiac workup because I was having chest pains and irregular heartbeats and whatnot, but they did not want to schedule it for me. I had to lie to them and say that, well, my cousin is a nurse, and she just thinks I should get it to rule things out. She listened to my heart, she said it didn't sound very good, and I might want to get it checked.

Which, of course, is what my naturopath told me, but if I said that to a doctor in Alberta, they'd be like, "Oh, a naturopath, well..."

So, they said for your peace of mind we'll do a stress test and a full workup. When I got there, I was waiting for the doctor and when he walked in the room, he laughed.

He apologized, of course, and said he's just not used to seeing people that young. I was sure he was going to send me home, but he saw that I had my stuff and was like, well, let's go ahead and do this.

I started on the treadmill, hooked up to the ECG machine and as he was watching the paper come out of the machine, his eyes almost popped out of his head. He was watching the paper and was like, "So, I'll be your cardiologist..."

It's still confusing to me because it seemed like there was some type of electrical issue. I was having extra beats and skipping beats, and when my heart rate increased it got really irregular, which is why I got the symptoms like tingling and chest pain, and so forth.

There was no real diagnosis, they said I had PVCs and an arrhythmia, and something was wrong electrically but they weren't sure what. From my own research, I've always thought it's probably Lyme Carditis, and my naturopaths have always treated my heart problems very seriously because I have Lyme. But when I tell medical doctors, they immediately dismiss me.

Lyme isn't an actual diagnosis here, so I have a diagnosis for CFS and fibromyalgia, but when doctors don't see a "real" diagnosis or evidence of one, they don't really believe me. Like most people, the diagnosis of chronic fatigue and fibro don't really do much.

Are you currently under medical care?

I do still have the connection with my naturopath in Vancouver, but I don't see her much now because I'm doing a lot better. I think the heart problems are permanent damage. I still can't have, like, even trace amounts of caffeine or let my body temperature get too elevated or my heart goes crazy. Other than that, I'm doing quite well.

How did you get from there to here?

After my heart problems and the IV antibiotics in Vancouver, I decided to enroll in college and ended up doing really well. I wasn't symptom-free, but I had really understanding instructors. I was still missing a lot of class and didn't have academic accommodations, but I got lucky with good instructors. I couldn't get accommodations without proper diagnosis documentation, and the mental work involved in trying to get that was just too much for me.

I did two years of visual arts and it was going really well, so I decided to transfer into industrial design and move to Vancouver. But then, as soon as I moved, it all came crashing down again and my health got worse.

Let me backup a little. When I was still living in Alberta and going to college there, I started on disulfiram. My mom had been researching it and decided it would be a good fit. My naturopath wasn't entirely sure about it, but I convinced her (mostly mom, actually, convinced her) to let me try it. I started at a low dose like you do, but I had to do it a lot slower because I was sensitive to the medication.

It caused a lot more of my sweats, brain fog, and fatigue issues. I don't think it really made my heart any worse, but all my other symptoms got worse. But then, they would start to get a little better, and once it starts to plateau, you increase the dose. I never got to the target dose because when I moved to Vancouver, my health crashed. The move was extremely stressful and I was miserable the entire time I was there.

I think the main thing was the environment there is just so damp. There's just so much mold in the air and the environment, and it rains every single day in the winter in Vancouver. Nothing ever has time to dry. I looked really hard to find a newer apartment with no basement, no major issues, and something that was the least likely to have mold. Even our sidewalk out front was green with algae year-round because nothing had time to dry.

I had been having a lot of really good days and doing big projects before I moved. Once I got to Vancouver, it wasn't long before even getting out of bed was too hard. I started reducing my course load and by November, just a month in, I had to defer from the program because I was too sick. I stopped the disulfiram while I was there because my heart started getting really bad. I basically had chest pain 24/7.

I stopped all the Lyme-killing treatment and basically did the mold detox. I was also on everything possible for anxiety because I was so anxious, which probably didn't help my Lyme either. I was trying to meditate but I was always agitated, felt like my adrenaline was always running, and constantly had a lump in my throat.

Having to defer from my dream program was upsetting, but it didn't cause the anxiety or anything like that. I was just anxious. I was finding things to be anxious about.

Once I deferred from the program, I decided to stay a few more months for some treatment since my naturopath was there. I did a month of IV antibiotics, traveling by train about an hour to the clinic each day, doing a full day of antibiotics, and then returning home. I did this every day for a month, all by myself because my boyfriend was working.

And of course, this was also during the height of COVID, so that added to the anxiety of being sick and being out in the world and all that. I had never been on public transit before, so I was really proud of myself that not only had I figured it out, but I was doing it alone. It was nice to feel independent, even if just for a minute.

How has Lyme impacted your life?

It's impacted my life in so many ways. When I realized that

I couldn't do college, I decided that if I could, I was going to do something I wanted to do. I had to give up industrial design, but I'm back to visual arts, which is where my passion is, anyway. Most of my high school I was sick so I missed out on a lot. I spent a lot of time traveling to doctors and didn't spend much time with friends or doing the typical things.

I had a big group of friends in high school. Looking back, I guess I was in the popular group, you could say. I was hanging out with people every day, seeing them at school, always having plans, etc. And then I started getting sick and most of them were not understanding or just couldn't get what was going on.

When my illness really started picking up, that's when I started dating my boyfriend, so I think they thought I was prioritizing him over them, but really I just couldn't do anything. I had a lot of falling outs and lost most of my friends from high school. A few stuck around, but not many. One friend I figure skated with when I was younger remained close and we're still really close today.

How has Lyme impacted other relationships?

I started dating my boyfriend the year I got diagnosed. I've known him since kindergarten because we live in a small town, but we didn't start dating until high school. He's been there with me the entire way, pretty much, and he's been amazing throughout all of it.

He moved with me to Vancouver and moved back and now has moved to Calgary with me. Since he watched me go through so much because he was always there, he does help remind me that things did happen when I forget or try to tell myself it didn't or it wasn't that bad. He's really supportive and I couldn't imagine this without him.

My mom and I are much closer. She is my advocate and once she understood that something was wrong, she dove into research and made it her full-time job to figure out what was wrong with me. She also became a huge advocate and member of the Lyme community once I got that diagnosis, which had made a lot of connections to help me get better.

My dad was the one that took me to Vancouver the first time. We had a good bonding experience around that, and we've always been really close and shared my love of art. He's also been a huge supporter of my art.

I have two brothers. My older brother had just gone off to university during all this so we weren't super close at the time. He's always been very understanding though and never once questioned me like so many others did. My younger brother and I were always really close when he was young. He's 16, so about 9 years younger than me. Mom would call me his mini-mom. It was hard when I got sick because he was young and didn't understand.

I remember him asking me one day when I was going to get better, and that was really tough. But, he's older now and he's a teenager, so we've grown apart a bit and he's kind of off doing his own thing. But we still get along well.

Have you made any friends along your Lyme journey?

I have met a few people through Instagram. The first friend I talked to that had Lyme was living in Arizona at the time. Our stories were so similar and it was crazy to talk to someone who had been through the exact same things, especially after never having talked to anyone who really understood it, let alone went through it.

Through her, I started talking with someone who lived in the same city as me. Last spring, I went to Greece with this friend on vacation. We went island hopping and spent a lot of time on the beach. I was there for about three weeks, I think. She stayed for a couple of months.

Are you on any current medications or have any routines for your Lyme?

Ever since I did the second round of IV treatment, once I was able to recover, it's been really good since then. I'm only on one medication: low dose naltrexone, for pain. I started that in Vancouver in 2018. I do still take a few supplements here and there, but not as many.

Making art is also really important for me. It's good for my mental health to be making things. It feels like when I'm not making art, or if I were to do something else with my life, it would be denying myself of something.

I'm in Calgary, about a nine-hour drive from home, going to school for visual arts again. This has been the best year so far. My program is great, I've made a lot of friends, and I'm feeling the best I have in a long time.

Are you hopeful for a cure or the future of Lyme disease patients?

I think it's tough. I don't know if there will ever be a magic medication or anything, but I'm really hopeful that there will be more research and education in the medical system, because it's pretty dire at the moment, especially in Canada.

I hope that at one point, you'll be able to walk into a hospital or doctor's office and say, "I have chronic Lyme" and get educated, proper treatment. That would be great, honestly.

How do you think sharing your story will help?

I think it's the most important thing with Lyme. If I had not talked to someone else who knew about Lyme, I wouldn't have gotten diagnosed. Doctors aren't helpful, so it's really through word-of-mouth and increasing awareness, which is so important.

Any advice or words you want to share with others?

It's really important to hear about success stories. When I was sick, I didn't even know that was possible. I really only heard of people who were still struggling with it, and I had very little hope of ever recovering because of that.

It's valid that you do have a chronic illness and that it does completely change your life, but I don't think that you have to give up hope.

You
Are Your
Best
Advocate .

JANEY CRINGEAN

Livingston, West Lothian, Scotland

Intelligent

Focused

Achieving

Janey was referred to me by another Lymie I interviewed. She resides in Scotland and has been not only battling her own Lyme disease, but working to advocate for better treatment for everyone in Scotland, since the Scottish NHS is one of the systems that doesn't even recognize the existence of Chronic Lyme. Janey's story is one that resonates with me because of the gaslighting and feelings of isolation. It's also just one part of her larger efforts toward spreading awareness and connecting those suffering from Lyme so they know they're not alone.

What are three words that describe you?

I'd say intelligent, focused, and achieving.

Do you have a song that inspired you through this journey?

'O Mio Babbino Caro' from Puccini's opera Gianni Schicchi.

Where did your journey begin?

I was 42 years old, symptoms started in early March 2004, about 10 days after a tick bite. I had a boil-like rash and severe vomiting and chills. I remember where I was when I got the tick. I was in Beecraigs Country Park in West Lothian, in between the play area and the deer park.

The rash started 10 days later, accompanied by a full day of severe vomiting and flu-like symptoms. As the rash persisted, I went to the GP a few weeks later. He immediately asked me: "Have you been anywhere in America where you could have got Lyme disease?" He thought it was only possible to be infected in America. His ignorance that you could get it in the UK was my missed opportunity for early treatment.

What symptoms did you experience?

Initially, I only had vague symptoms. Headaches began about 10 months after the bite. Three years after the bite, they were so excruciating it was like having a sharp knife twisted into my head and I thought my eye was going to explode. I had a stiff neck, pelvic and rib pain, and terrible fatigue. I needed help getting out of chairs, I had difficulty rolling over in bed, and I couldn't stay awake long enough to eat a meal. Then I started getting worrying tremors, peripheral neuropathy, balance issues, and terrible tinnitus. My illness has been the neurological form of Lyme.

What was your journey to a diagnosis like?

After the first doctor's visit, I had three years of misdiagnosis before I collapsed completely. During that time, the rash was frozen off by a dermatologist but grew back and expanded. It was then excised by my then-new GP and sent off for biopsy but was not tested for Lyme disease. The rash grew back and kept expanding, lasting 14 months before it spontaneously disappeared. I was referred to a gynecologist and a rheumatologist, but nobody could work out what was wrong.

Remembering my first GP's questions, I started investigating Lyme disease. I soon worked out that the characteristic bulls-eye rash was diagnostic for Lyme. When I asked the rheumatologist, he told me that if I had had it for more than a year, they wouldn't treat me anyway and so there was no point in testing. My GP also refused to test me. There were so many missed opportunities because of the lack of public awareness materials, and ignorance of UK incidence, the initial symptoms, the significance of the rash, and the fact that Lyme can persist for years without treatment.

After three years, I sat in my GP surgery, demanding to be referred to Infectious Diseases to be assessed for Lyme. Finally, he relented. The Infectious Diseases consultant did a battery of tests, all of which were negative. He then told me I had Bannwarth's Syndrome, a neurological syndrome associated with Borrelia garinii, and diagnosed probable Lyme disease. He said I had a high level of antibodies, but they could not identify what they were.

I have since found out Borrelia garinii was not being tested for at the time. He also told me I was lucky to have had the rash or I would get a diagnosis of MS. In 2014, two separate private tests from different accredited laboratories in the US gave positive results for Borrelia garinii. In late 2017, private Elispot tests from Germany were positive for Borrelia, Bartonella, Babesia and Anaplasma.

It was the first time I had had such tests for co-infections. My current NHS consultant does not accept the tests as they were done abroad. But I have not had an NHS test for Bartonella or Anaplasma and have only been tested for one species of Babesia. I have never tested positive in any NHS test for Lyme, despite having a diagnostic bulls-eye rash, sufficient to have been given a clinical diagnosis.

How many doctors did you see before reaching your official diagnosis?

I saw a total of seven doctors: two GPs and five consultants (dermatology, gynecology, rheumatology, ENT, and an ID consultant).

What was the treatment journey like?

Finally, virtually bed bound after three years of illness, I started oral antibiotic treatment and began to improve, but it only kept the illness at bay, and I relapsed badly when I tried to stop them.

I asked if I could be treated with the intravenous antibiotics which were recommended at the time for neurological Lyme disease, but my request was refused. I paid for a private consultation with a senior NHS neurologist, but he told me he did not believe in the existence of chronic Lyme disease and that I should explore psychological avenues. Eventually, after more than three years of treatment, I saw a new Infectious Diseases consultant. Within five minutes of meeting him, his words were "There is no doubt you've had Lyme disease but you have had the recommended treatment. There is nothing more we can do. You are discharged."

I was sent home, unable to stop taking antibiotics without relapsing badly, expecting to die without them, and without further help. My GP asked him to reconsider, but he refused. My GP then asked another consultant for a second opinion. He refused to see me because my serology was negative. Because two consultants refused to help me, my GP also refused to help further.

I was left with no option but to seek private treatment. The guidelines of the International Lyme and Associated Disease Society are currently the only guidelines listed in the US National Guidelines Clearinghouse. They acknowledge chronic Lyme and the need for longer treatment with multiple antibiotics. I found a doctor who followed them. I started on three antibiotics at once and had a very strong die-off reaction initially.

After a few months, I realized I was beginning to feel better. Gradually, I was able to get my life back. However, treatment has involved much more than just antibiotics. I have also been careful about nutrition and taken supplements to break down the bacterial biofilm that Lyme hides in, to support the broken biochemical pathways in my body, and to give constant support to my severely weak and damaged immune system. Each intervention has been another small step to improvement, but to this day I still need treatment.

In 2018, after further testing revealed I was suffering not just from Lyme disease, but Babesia, Bartonella and Anaplasma, treatment was stepped up to cover those illnesses too. Finally, I am seeing light at the end of the tunnel.

What did you do to distract yourself during this time?

Reading, gardening, and photography really kept me occupied and gave me something to enjoy at a time when I had very little joy in my life.

How has Lyme impacted your life?

This illness has had a devastating impact on my life. I have not worked full-time since 2006. Many others have had to give up work completely. But by 2014, after over three years of private treatment, I felt significantly better and started having energy to do more. I have been able to build up my social life again. I can now manage a fairly normal existence so long as I give myself plenty of time in the mornings before starting my day.

I still get headaches, fatigue, brain, sinus and eye issues, and my body feels like it is on fire, but many of the other symptoms have gone. I am one of the lucky ones as I can afford private treatment. I may not be fully recovered but at least I have a much better quality of life.

However, that wasn't always the case.

I spent six months struggling just to get to the bathroom and back, unable to even eat a meal without falling asleep.

I had four years where I needed help getting out of chairs and struggled to roll over in bed.

For seven years, I was almost unable to get out of the house and had no social life.

And for 16 years, I was unable to work full-time because of my Lyme disease.

I have had to modify my expectations in almost every area of my life. My husband had to take the reins (and strain) of running our business. I had to reduce my expectations of myself and what I could achieve. We were largely unable to deal with clients and lost a lot of work, so we eventually stopped employing others.

Lyme hasn't really impacted my relationships, but it did change my marriage dynamic slightly because I no longer had the strength I did originally.

How long have you had Lyme disease?

All told, I have been suffering from Lyme disease for 19 years.

Has your family been supportive through your Lyme journey?

I have very supportive parents and my husband is an amazing support.

Have you found any friends or support along the way?

I have met other Scottish patients through my own re-search and advocacy efforts. Most of my support has come from my husband, but there was one private consultant that did offer some assistance. I also helped my consultant start a Scottish Lyme charity called Lyme Resource Centre, but I had to pull out after two years because it was too much for me to handle.

What current treatments, routines, and health practices do you have?

I take antibiotics and supplements to the tune of about 40 tablets each day. I also use herbal powders and tinctures to help boost my immune system and combat the Lyme symptoms. I have regular infrared sauna treatments, weekly acupuncture, and regular RIFE treatments, as well.

How does having Lyme, an "invisible" illness, impact you emotionally?

It's been extremely difficult. I've withdrawn from most NHS Scotland care because I've been too traumatized. I've been laughed at by consultants, told I'm "addicted to antibi-otics," and even been threatened with being referred to a psychologist against my will.

I've been told that many people think they have Lyme, despite the fact that the NHS doesn't even really recognize it, but it's not usually the case. I had a lot of anxiety and depression during the initial diagnostic journey and treat-ment process, but I have started to manage that better, as well.

When you think about the future of Lyme patients, are you hopeful there is a cure?

Yes, eventually I hope there will be a cure. I don't think it's anything that will happen in the short-term, though. I think it will take some time.

How do you feel (or hope) that sharing your story will help?

I am sharing my story to help with my efforts in persuading non-believers that chronic Lyme exists and involves bacterial persistence.

Any words of advice, encouragement, etc. that you'd like to offer the rest of the Lyme community?

It's not all in your head. Don't give up trying to be believed.

Fact:

Lyme can be transmitted

in less than 24 hours

ANABEL VIDAL

Buenos Aires, Argentina

Resilient

Fighter

Conscientious

Anabel resides in Argentina, and has had two separate stages of her Lyme disease journey. She gleaned insights from pop culture icons Justin Bieber and Avril Lavigne, and is one of the lucky ones who actually saw her tick and had immediate symptoms from her bite. However, it still kept her from getting an accurate diagnosis for more than six years and resulted in six months of being completely bedridden. Let's dive into her story.

What are three words that describe you?

Three words that describe me would be resilient, fighter, and conscientious. I'd also say I'm supportive if I can have four.

Do you have a song that inspired you through this journey?

"Revolution", by Abel Pintos.

Where did your journey begin?

I think my journey has had two stages. The first was in 2014. I was 28 at the time, in the middle of a personal crisis that had destabilized me emotionally. I asked my husband to take me out of Buenos Aires because at that moment my head was shooting with many intrusive thoughts (as if the idea of being 700 or 1,000 kilometers away could minimally avoid the bomb that exploded around me).

We visited the province where my husband lived for many years before we met and after a few days, we did 300 more kilometers to spend time with some friends. We went to the Province of Mendoza (at that time we were 1,000 kilometers from Buenos Aires), and we were invited to go spend a day in the countryside at the "RIO BLANCO" ban.

We left the car on the road, and we went down a slope full of branches and grassland. It was from there that after eight hours of scratching my rib on the side of the heart, because of what I thought was a clothing tag, I decided something wasn't right.

We were already in the vehicle, driving along, and I was itching and starting to feel a stinging pain. Finally, I asked my husband to check me because it stung me too much, and he found the tick attached to my body. He pulled the tick out, ensuring to get it completely, and then disposed of it. Then, he mentioned Lyme disease, but I said, "No, that's only in the U.S. The deer tick."

I knew that Avril Lavigne had Lyme, and she knew that it was caused by the bite of a tick. However, she never provided much additional insight on the condition, and I was unaware of the existence of Lyme cases in Argentina. Exactly a week later, on Saturday, we were going to spend the day in a cabin with a pool. It was really hot, so we decided to have lunch and then take a short nap in the air conditioning before going to the pool—but my "nap" lasted until 8 PM.

They came to pick me up and took me to the pool. I approached the edge of the pool and laid down. I covered myself with a towel because I felt cold and went back to sleep. My body hurt, my head hurt, I had chills, and it was at that moment that I realized what was happening was not "normal."

I told my husband to give me the thermometer and my temperature was reading 104 degrees Fahrenheit. We were far from the city, so I took a fever reducer and they helped me lower the fever with ice and cold cloths. I didn't bother going to the city, but I don't think it would've made much of a difference. I had brought a souvenir in Erythema Migrans that caused me itching for six months and a bacteria that was feasting on my body. My head was not in a place to think about what had happened.

The second part of my journey came in January 2020, six years later. Justin Bieber announced that he had chronic Lyme disease. Instagram awareness campaigns were launched and that led me to a post by Avril Lavigne where she explained that the presence of MS could equal Lyme. And she listed some symptoms, of which I had all but two:

- Flu with fever and chills
- Headache and neck pain
- Fatigue and trouble sleeping
- Nausea
- Abdominal swelling
- Gastritis
- Arthritis
- Joint pain
- Sensitivity to sound and light
- Swollen glands
- Chest pain
- Muscle pain
- Irritability
- Depression
- Memory problems
- Brain fog
- Anxiety
- Focus and cognitive issues
- Anger and aggression
- Lack of balance
- Confusion and disorientation

- Seizures (I did not have these)
- Bell's Palsy (I also did not have this)

That night, as I laid awake with insomnia, I decided to do some research. I went to Google and looked up "Lyme in Argentina" and the first result was the story of Pablo P., my "angel" and someone who helped me in more ways than he knows.

I read his story, thank God. It resonated so much that I left my contact phone and sent him a WhatsApp message that summarized my symptoms and the history of my tick bite. We had a call the following Saturday at 8 AM and we talked for two hours. He's from Mendoza, which is where I got bitten, so he was able to recommend a laboratory in Caba that was 30 minutes from my house.

On January 15, 2020, I did the extraction Immunofluorescence IGG and IGM for Borrelia Burgdorferi. On January 20 my results arrived. I was positive for the IGM. I joined the Lyme Argentina group, and a week later I started my treatment journey.

What was your journey to a diagnosis like?

I didn't even really see a doctor much at first. I didn't want to deal with it after the initial bite and was not ready to consider the possibility of severe consequences, so I tried to let it go. Even though I was already in contact with Lyme Argentina and a specialty doctor that understood Lyme, I still managed to live sick for about six years. I was bouncing from one doctor to the next, hospitalized, in medical guards, or getting told I wasn't really sick at all.

When I arrived at Dr. Brizuela's office for the first time, I went with my analysis in hand (the Lyme test). That same day, I left the office with Doxycycline, Apitoxin injections, and IV vitamin supplements prescribed for about 15 days later.

How many doctors did you see before reaching your official diagnosis?

I saw tons of doctors. I don't even know the exact number. For six years, I practically lived at the doctor's. I was always sick, but my health continued to deteriorate and when I would try to discuss it, they would blame it on stress.

How did you feel when you were first diagnosed?

I was very emotional about it all. It was nice to finally have an answer, but it was also a lot to take in. We spent two hours talking with the doctor about transmission, generation, treatments, generalities, children, and so forth. I remember returning on the highway, crying in an almost silent way, watching the landscape go by. We went on for several kilometers that way, both of us just crying and trying to figure out what was going on. We were emotionally discharging until we were able to talk.

Once we could talk, we made the decision at that moment to fight. There was no option to quit. We had to go through this and we had to fight with everything we had.

What was the treatment journey like?

The journey was long, but once I had the analysis and that diagnosis, it was irrefutable. She has Lyme. The treatment started with Doxycycline 100, two tablets per day for 12 months, along with a stomach protector because long-term antibiotics can wreak havoc on the stomach. After an ultrasound and fatty liver test, we added four tablets of two additional medications, three injections, and one ml of Apitoxin.

Twice a week, the nurse visited me and gave me IV vitamins that were indicated by the doctor. These were huge doses of vitamins, including a lot of Vitamin C. I ended up spending my entire salary on the treatment, setting up a nursing station next to my bed, buying supplies, and outfitting my home to work as a place I could be "treated" for my Lyme disease.

Currently, I consume about 12 tablets a day and have other treatments, as well.

What was your official diagnosis and how long have you had Lyme?

I was officially diagnosed with Chronic Lyme in 2020, but I have had it since 2014. This January (2023) is nine years since I first contracted the disease.

How has Lyme impacted your life?

In the six years prior to getting a diagnosis, I was in and out of the doctors' offices, had several hospitalizations, and suffered from a variety of physical and mental ailments, including anxiety and panic attacks that were both symptoms of the Lyme and induced by the Lyme, to a certain degree, because there is so much unknown about it. In 2019, a few months before my diagnosis, I had noticed my legs were getting very numb. I had to move them or change position every few minutes or they were unable to move entirely.

In 2018, I tried to turn in bed and the room spun. I had to ask my husband and son for help to the bathroom, and then ask them to take me to emergency. Something wasn't right. I was hospitalized, but they gave me IV diazepam claiming that I had a panic attack (at this point I was an expert in panic attacks, and that was not such). After many hours, I was sent home and told to see an otolaryngologist.

That specialist said that surely the otoliths of the ear had moved, but the audiometry was excellent. They medicated me with something that made me nauseous. I had such a bad time that I stopped taking it. The initial episode lasted a week, and then it came and went from one day to the next.

By the end of 2019, my dyslexia with writing and speaking was becoming worrisome, as was my memory loss. I was struggling at work and confiding in my husband that I was worried it wasn't going to improve. After starting treatment, of course, everything got worse. I had no strength, no balance, and couldn't even walk to the bathroom, let alone take care of myself. I started losing my hair, too, and that was very depressing for me.

I didn't manage to get out of bed for about six months. Since I couldn't do much, though, I started learning about Lyme, putting together networks, raising awareness, and helping the community. It was all behind the scenes until I wrote a local newspaper and made my story public. This also helped me discern a rash on my son's back, who was bitten by a tick in 2008 at age three.

The positive impact Lyme has had would be in the spiritual strengthening. I have personally suffered situations of gender and psychological violence by the father of my son (who is not my husband), and I think that if I survived all that, the bacteria will not defeat me!

It also gave me the tools to help many people, mainly my son, to give him the example of solidarity, and the struggle for principles, for beliefs, to always fight. Lyme made me mature and see life from another perspective. I understand that today I cannot go back in time. Nothing will change what already happened nine years ago, but it is in me how to take all this, learn from my situation, and make the best of it. The "why this happens to me" was never part of my questions, but "that I have to learn from this" and that I could remain positive throughout.

How has Lyme impacted your relationships?

Many people have not believed in me over the years. I also moved away to get away from the issues I was having and the toxic people in the family. At first, it was difficult for supportive people like my parents to understand, but they never stopped supporting me for a second. I think it actually strengthened our bond, as it did with my partner and son.

I also made several virtual friends at this time, built a Lyme family, and connected with many people around the world.

Do you feel that you've missed out on anything because of Lyme?

I have tried on many occasions to study. I started nine years ago and it was put on pause. My work has also been on hiatus for three years. Having time, making choices, and scheduling things is difficult because you never know how your day is going to be.

Has your family been supportive through your Lyme journey?

My parents had the hardest time at first. They didn't understand the risks in the pandemic, or how far Lyme can go. I get they thought it was not as serious as everyone was saying, so they refused to watch videos or consume information on the subject. Over time, however, they came around and began to understand my struggle. My husband and son have always been very supportive, and I am lucky to have so many good people in my life.

Have you found any friends or support along the way?

Pablo P. is actually the one that helped me the most. The one who gave me the basics, the laboratory information, the doctor, and the support. I know he's a busy person, but I also know that if I need him, he's just a phone call away. There aren't enough words to thank him for all he taught me, and I don't mean just with Lyme, but with his entire state of being. He makes me feel down to earth and his words of encouragement and example of strength have shaped my own journey.

Without him I would not have the diagnosis I have or the information to be able to help my son. I have also have many other points of support in the Argentine Lyme group, and it would be unfair if I named some and not all.

What have you tried in terms of treatment and what has helped?

I have tried antibiotics, injectable apitoxin, orthomolecular medicine, paleo diet, fasting, and detox. After understanding what helped my body and what made me able to get out of bed, I dabbled in Bee Venom Therapy, and changed my life. Today I am about to add the protocol of Dr. Bob Beck with Zapper.

The paleolithic diet helped me a lot, but after a complicated 2022 that included the amputation of my ring finger and metacarpal, and having gained weight, I started (thanks to Nutrilyme) a ketogenic diet accompanied by fasting.

What kinds of things did you do to distract yourself during treatments?

During the three years after the diagnosis, I spent a lot of time in bed. I used the PC to design things to support the Lyme community and Lyme Argentina, including designing their logo. I made t-shirts, flyers, learning and reading materials, and other resources.

I also did a lot of learning and reading on my own. I am a huge fan of reading and thank God for all the neuro Lyme symptoms, I didn't lose my sight or concentration for reading. However, the same isn't true with TV. It's hard for me to concentrate on shows so I don't watch a lot.

Once I could get out of bed, I returned to cooking, drawing, and painting. I even renovated a small bathroom by painting it.

What current treatments, routines, and health practices do you have?

The diet I had to give up in 2022, but I still do many other things. I take Epsom salt baths, do detox, drink juices with magnesium and collagen, do dry brushing and facial cleansing, and soak up the sun. Helping myself feel better in general seems to do wonders. I also use enemas when I have digestive issues, but that's only on occasion. And as I mentioned, I still take a lot of medications and supplements.

One of the things I do that makes me happiest is to support others and take an active role in Lyme Argentina and the entire Lyme community.

How did having Lyme, an "invisible" illness, impact you emotionally?

I think that emotionally, the fact that I have lived through the treatment of many doctors, professionals, and even a psychiatrist, crying to all of them, has been positive. Dealing with those who didn't believe me, even when I had an analysis in hand, was very toxic, but I don't let them get me down. Instead, I fight from a different perspective. In some cases, I have managed to make a difference. Others are still in need of some work.

Certain doctors have not hesitated for a second, and once I had their support, I was more confident about walking out on doctors who weren't going to listen or believe me. I do not waste my time and do not want to be working with anyone who is not supportive of Lyme and helping me get the care I need. I try to educate in all areas of my life. I had my fair share of depression and "down" days, but seeing how I can make a difference makes a big difference for me.

I am the owner of deciding how to fight my battle and I choose to be grateful and mindful, even though the road is difficult on many days. Even on my roughest days, getting on my computer and connecting with other Lyme patients would do wonders for my mood and spirit.

When you think about the future of Lyme patients, are you hopeful there is a cure?

This is a controversial one. The pharmaceutical industry is a business. Not only because of Lyme, but they just do not see it in their work to help people in general. They want to sell their products and get rich. I don't believe in vaccines. I don't believe in the pharmaceutical industry doing something selfless for patients who, as they continue to be sick, consume more.

Besides that, we know what the recognition of Lyme as a disease would involve: lawsuits and more lawsuits. In Argentina, there is no predisposition to dialogue for Lyme. I believe that the cure will come in helping us make the best decisions for our individual bodies. Unfortunately, we must learn to live with this, doing so in the best possible way.

How do you feel (or hope) that sharing your story will help?

Every opportunity to share my story is a chance to help someone else. I have participated in YouTube interviews, newspaper articles, online interviews, radio, and other networks. I hope to soon be on TV since I couldn't do it in 2022, but I will continue to share my story everywhere I can. If it helps even one person, I will feel like it has done its job.

Any words of advice, encouragement, etc. that you'd like to offer the rest of the Lyme community?

If you fail one day, do not forget that you can also learn from bad days. Only you know how difficult your battle is and I congratulate you for moving forward every day. Especially those days that are uphill. Accepting that you can't handle everything every day is also a part of the healing process. Being positive isn't about being happy all the time. It's about understanding that even though there are difficult days, better days will come.

Be grateful ALWAYS. Be grateful for what you have, for what was not given, for what has changed you and improved you.

Be thankful for what you did not expect and how strong you have shown yourself to be.

Be thankful that although you may not be where you want to be, every single day is a new possibility to get closer or start over.

If you don't see the greatness in you, no one else will see it.

If you don't think you shine, no one else will notice you.

If you are not satisfied, no one else will satisfy you.

Everything starts with you. And if one day, you need to cry, do it if that helps you. However, after you're done, get up and move on.

Never forget how far you've come and everything that you have overcome.

Remember all the times you tried hard even when you felt like you couldn't.

Every time you got out of bed, no matter how hard it was.

All the times you wanted to give up but you just kept going one more time.

Never forget that strength. That resilience.

"I believe that nothing happens by chance. Deep down, things have their own secret plan, even though we don't understand it."

—Carlos Ruiz Zafón, The Shadow of the Wind

And finally, I want to quote part of the song "Rezo Por Vous" by Luis Alberto Spinetta:

"I pray, pray for you, pray for you, that's why I pray for you... that's why I pray."

Shout Out

To the people who :

Fight a daily battle others can't see

KATHRYN WALKER

Hamburg, Germany

Brave

Witty

Kind

Kathryn's story is probably one of the scariest for us fellow Lymies, and yet it's all too common. She was lumped into the "maybe it's psychological" category, hospitalized against her will, and fought through all kinds of horrible doctors to get the diagnosis and treatment she needed. She lives in Hamburg, Germany, in a flat that she loves in an ideal location. However, Lyme has made her life far from ideal.

What are three words that describe you?

I would say brave, witty, and kind.

Is there a song that inspires you or has helped you?

I wouldn't even say an entire song, but a line from a song. It's "Constant Craving" by K.D. Lang, and the line goes:

"Even through the darkest phase

be it thick or thin

always someone marches brave

here beneath my skin."

I've always found that powerful and it has helped me in my own fight.

When did your Lyme journey begin?

I might have had an inkling that I got bitten in like 1999, but I didn't really notice anything wrong until the summer of 2002. I lived in a rural town. I had gotten a job at the one translation company they had there. I used to go jogging in the woods before work, and everything was fine. I was happy in my own little world. When I was in England, I was a freelance translator and freelance German teacher, which was very unreliable income. Here, I had a fixed income, which was great, and I also had other translators and colleagues around.

In Germany, you get six weeks of holiday, and I would collect all my holidays and take six weeks off and go explore the world. I went to Nepal, New Zealand, Indonesia, etc. I was living out what I really wanted to do, traveling and living abroad. I had a great time.

Then, in the summer of 2002, I remember there was a meeting of pain in the left side of my brain above my ear. Pain was shooting through my head. The pains came very quickly and were happening once every few minutes or so. I remember getting up and saying to my colleague, "Do you know of any doctors?"

He suggested a doctor that was right around the corner, and I went to see him. I had always been healthy up to this point, so I never really needed a doctor or saw them much for anything. This doctor did a brain scan, but only because when he asked if I had other symptoms, I told him that sometimes I get migraine auras without the pain. But otherwise, I didn't have any other symptoms.

The shooting pains were strange, coming on so quickly and eventually fading away. They subsided to a few hours, then a few days, and then were just gone as quickly as they came. I just wanted to forget about it, really, even though it was such an unusual event. Then, I noticed that I had a rash. And nothing made this rash go away. I focused on this new job thing because I was trying to get a new job and I didn't know what else to do in regard to the rash.

I went for an interview in Hamburg around Easter 2003,

and got the job. I left my company in June 2003 and had a bit of holiday before I started my new job in July. I went to England, and then I went to Houston to visit my friend James who had just moved there. I remember that I could get stuff there that I couldn't get here, so I bought this over-the-counter cream for this rash, but it didn't really help, either. Then, when I came back from holiday, everything went like clockwork.

Finding an apartment in Hamburg isn't usually easy, but I got lucky. I rang a friend of a friend, and asked, "How do you find an apartment in Hamburg?"

She asked if our mutual friend had said something, because at that time she was looking for someone to rent her apartment while she was away for two months. So, I moved in there and pretty quickly, I found the apartment that I'm still in today, nearly 20 years later.

Everything was going great. My new colleagues were great. One of them worked at the old company with me, so I knew someone there from the start. I had really landed in clover and was sailing, career-wise. But at the same time, I was really not feeling well at all.

What were the first symptoms or signs of Lyme disease that you noticed?

Because of the rash I mentioned, which was in a private area, I went to the gynecologist. They don't link a rash like that with Lyme disease. They just gave me all kinds of creams but it never went away. Nothing helped. Then, eventually, she decided it was lichens sclerosus, but they couldn't actually pinpoint a cause. I think now, looking back, the trigger was a tick bite.

Around November 2003, I went to a doctor in Hamburg. I was concerned because the first symptoms that I had were in my brain. Then, I started developing negative thoughts. My life is amazing, I'm being paid a good salary and I've got a great flat and it's in a lovely area. But I have negative, intrusive, really dark thoughts. I was thinking of suicide, suddenly and out of nowhere, but there was absolutely no reason.

I went to the doctor and said, "I'm concerned about how I'm thinking. Can you keep an eye on me?" And she did a blood test, and when she got the results, she told me something I'd never heard:

"Oh, you've got borrelia in your blood."

She, of her own accord, did this test the Eliza test. And it came back positive. So I asked, what's borrelia? And she said, you must have had a tick bite. I knew what the word was, but I didn't know what a tick was exactly- I just knew it was a bug, that was all. I was so worried about my retention at that point that I was taking notes while speaking to her.

Then she said, "You can get it checked in three months' time if you want."

I thought, well, she said if you like, so it's really no big deal, just go back and get a re-check. I didn't really worry about it beyond that. Then, at the end of my six-month probationary period, I had to go through a sort of check-up. Everyone does it at their six-month mark; it's a large engineering company that sends people all over the world, so they have a sick bay and a doctor on site. At my checkup, they asked if anything was going on, and I told them about my other visit. Their blood test came back for borrelia, as well.

As a side note, I have to say this. Lyme disease is the most trivialized illness in Germany. I actually saw that on the Federal German Republic's website, it was on there for several years.

So, anyway, the doctor in sick bay says, "Oh yeah, your immune system deals with it, it's fine."

So of course, I went out thinking that I was fine.

I went out thinking I was fine. If you'd have put everything together, it might have added up more quickly. Things were starting to add up, but no one was connecting the dots. No one asked all the right questions and brought everything together. I never even bothered to tell anyone because if the doctor says you're fine, you're fine. Meanwhile, I still had negative thoughts, racing thoughts, just horrific mental issues. Then, the rage started.

I thought, I've got to do something. I don't know what's wrong with me, but I've got to do something with all this rage. I started doing what my passion was, was to run a bit more. I joined the company running club, and in September 2004, I did my first half-marathon. I joined a marathon training group. I ran the Belden Marathon in September 2005 and then came back and immediately signed up for the Hamburg Marathon in Spring 2006.

All this time, I had this terrible depression, and the rage was getting worse. I was sent to see psychiatrists and psychologists, and had some really nasty experiences. I remember going to one before work and trying to explain what was going on, and he said in German what essentially translated to, "You can't get a man into bed, that's your problem."

When I started crying at his rude comment, he said, "What act are you putting on now?"

I said, "I'm not putting on an act. I am sick."

Then, it just got worse… It's crazy that you're in a room with a guy in a suit and he's just saying these abusive things to you. You just can't believe it. Eventually, I got to a point where I stood up and said, "I'm sorry, I'm in the wrong place here."

And I went to leave, at which point he grabbed my arm and was like, "Oh I didn't mean it." and I just told him to forget it and walked out.

Another doctor sent me to this psychiatric hospital on the edge of town. I got up at 6 AM to take several trains and buses to this place, and it was an awful experience, too. This woman was crazy, she didn't even mention her name. She just opened the door and told me to come in and sit down.

She was just saying to me in German that I needed to speak more fluently, that I was stuttering, and so forth. I was like, what do you mean? Most people understand me and I'm pretty sure my German is close to perfect. It was a very bizarre conversation and interaction all around, devoid of any human understanding whatsoever.

I just got up, and said again, "I'm not in the right place."

I was really ill at the time, and I can remember walking down the hall of this hospital, just screaming. I walked outside, screaming, and screaming, and of course they all came out. Then, I just screamed at this woman, "What are you doing here??!?!? You've got to be trained in conversation skills! What was that?!?"

I remember seeing a nurse who was really calm and who was talking to me normally. She even told me that my German was perfect and I was speaking correctly and was not difficult to understand at all. But I came away once again with no answers.

I mentioned the marathon training group—someone from there knew a private psychiatrist and was able to get me an emergency appointment. I was anxious, but he was a nice man. He listened to me and everything, but it didn't matter because what I was saying wasn't really true. I wasn't depressed, anxious, or any of that. I was just having these thoughts and feelings because of a bacterial infection.

Fast-forward to April 2007, the Paris Marathon. While I was training for the marathon, I brought my own food for work. One day, instead, I went into the canteen and the boss was talking about someone he knew who was really ill with borrelia borreliosis. I was like, what, this is a serious illness? Didn't those doctors say I had this? I was thinking, are you saying this is a big deal? And I was just listening to him telling this story, thinking, is this my problem?

So, I ran the Paris Marathon and then my body collapsed. In retrospect, I was affecting my body, but I didn't realize it at the time. I was very fit up to that point and was taking what I thought was good care in my training. I got the flu-like symptoms, and then it really came out. My brain was just shutting down. The pressure in my brain was getting worse and I felt like everything was looking through glass. I remember looking out the window and my brain capacity seemed to suddenly go down.

269

Then, I went to visit a friend and she suggested that I visit a local doctor. I went and said, I think I have neuro-borreliosis. The doctor gave me some antibiotics, but then told me that I just needed to visit my doctor when I got home. And when I did, the doctor back home said, "Oh, no, you don't have that, because with borreliosis, you get facial paralysis and you don't have that."

She ignored everything else and made a decision based on that fact alone.

Then, I remember one evening I was cooking dinner for a friend and I could hardly speak. My brain was getting harder and harder (it felt like a stone) and I started to develop paralysis. My legs were going. I rang the emergency doctor, and when he came in, I was on the landing. He took one look at me and immediately started saying that I was mentally ill.

I said, "What do you mean? You haven't done any tests!"

I can remember being at work and my brain is like a stone and I can't do anything. But this doctor wouldn't listen. I called James, my friend who was in Houston, and asked him to talk to this doctor who has just pronounced me mentally ill. So, James gets on the phone and says in his best German, I don't think she's mentally ill, but I do think she needs help. So, the doctor told me to get my things and took me to the car.

I remember as I was going down the stairs, I remember the doctor saying, "Oh gosh, well if anything happens now, I'm responsible." It was like I was some sort of liability. But I managed to get down the stairs and he put me in his car and took me straight to psychiatry. This was in the

Summer of 2007. His plan was to get me to a psych hospital on the outskirts of town from the emergency hospital.

I remember that as I was trying to get into the ambulance, my arms and legs lost all control. I suddenly developed Ataxia and could not get into the ambulance on my own. This was in the middle of the night, probably three or four o'clock in the morning, and I was just lying on the concrete outside the hospital. At this point, my legs were completely paralyzed. A doctor in a white coat (from psych) came out and I remember this as clear as day:

He looked around to see if there was anybody around. Then, he looked down at me and said, "Stand up."

I said, "I can't, I'm paralyzed."

He turned around and went back into the building. Then, I started having a major epileptic fit. I thought my backbone was going to break. This scream came out of me, almost like an animal. Then, these people came back in white coats, probably about four of them, and they just picked me up and they took me back inside the hospital. they didn't say a word the entire time. Meanwhile, I'm asking what they're doing with me, begging them to please say something.

I said, "Look, I think I have neuroborreliosis."

They still said nothing.

Then, they took me into this side room and they started to tie me down. And I said, "Please don't do this." I was begging with them. I move a lot, I'm active, fit, and even as a kid, I was always moving and being active. As he got to my arm, I tried to stop him and was still asking them to stop and nothing.

I told them again, "I think I have neuroborreliosis. I think I'm dying."

He scoffed, and no one has ever died of a tick bite. It's just not true.

Then, they all walked out in silence.

I've always had a very Buddhist background, so I was like, okay, maybe this is my time. It's come, and that's okay. I was 46 at this point, so it wasn't a long life, but it was a good one for the most part. I called out and no one came. Then, a nurse suddenly appeared and asked if I wanted an injection or something to drink. I didn't want to be poked with a needle, so I said I'd like a drink. And then I was gone.

When I woke up, I was in the psych unit on the edge of town. It was a secure unit, kind of like a holding pen. I remember thinking, this is horrific... but then I remember seeing the patients playing chess. I decided I wanted to play to prove my mind still worked, and I remember I won. It's not all gone.

They put me on a ward for psychosis, so I said, "What kind of psychosis do I have?"

All I've got is that I'm struggling through something—my cognitive functions aren't there. There is pressure in my brain. I had a rash and a stiff neck. And their solution was to give me this little booklet that was like a questionnaire for psychosis. I got like five out of 29 or something, meaning I clearly wasn't dealing with mental issues—so why was I in the psychiatry unit?

Then, there was one doctor I talked to and he tested me, but for syphilis. I told him there was zero chance that I had syphilis. I wasn't in a relationship or anything, I wasn't exposed, and so forth. I was at the hospital for about two and a half or three weeks, but they did let me out. And while I was there, I was allowed out on occasion.

I had a laptop, but it was broken at that time, so I went to an Internet café and looked up neuroborreliosis for the first time. I just remember thinking, "Jesus, yeah I've got that."

"Yeah, I had a stiff neck."

"Yeah, I had a rash."

And so on, and so forth. But what do I do? I'm still in this psych hospital but I need different help. So, I rang ILADS and they gave me the number of a doctor in Denmark, who referred me to another doctor in Berlin. The doctor in Berlin was a tropical medicine doctor, and when I rang him, he wasn't the least bit surprised.

I said, "Hello, my name is Kathryn Walker, I'm being held in psychiatry, but I have all these symptoms and think I have neuroborreliosis."

"Oh, yes, yes, this happens all the time. And mind you, I'd worked for a health system in England for about a year, and a medical laboratory in Germany for another year. I'm "of the system," so to speak, so I naturally trusted the system. And now here's this doctor saying, well this happens.

I'm thinking, you get the wrong diagnosis, you get the wrong treatment—this is medicine??

He asked if I was taking the tablets and if they were helping. I said yes, I had to, but they weren't doing anything. I was actually getting worse and was afraid I was going to fall into a coma. He told me to keep the pills in my mouth and when they leave, spit them out. So I did that as much as I could, and after that two or three weeks, I signed myself out because I wasn't getting anywhere.

By that time, what I needed more than anything was to be treated like a human being. I booked a holiday in Scotland first thing. I took a week and visited Scotland and saw some people I knew. I needed that week just to feel like a human. When I got back, I went to Berlin to see that doctor. I felt like my brain capacity was at 25%, but at least I was there.

The thing is he had the disease himself, so he knew. He believed me and I was grateful for that. He prescribed antibiotics, but after about a month, it just kept getting worse. So I rang him and explained that I was going downhill.

"This is desperate. I don't have much longer. If I end up in a coma in this flat here, they won't think it's anything. We're talking like, 24 hours, and I might not be able to speak, walk, or do much of anything."

By this point, concepts were starting to crumble. I couldn't grasp days of the week and stuff like that. My brain was so limited that I couldn't handle the sensory overload of the world, so I didn't go out much. Even the Internet was huge and overwhelming, so I tried to avoid it as much as I could. But if you say anything like this to most doctors, they immediately want to send you to psych.

He told me to come to his private office in Dusseldorf, so I did. I'm still not sure how I made that journey. He gave me some medication, and I was grateful because I could stay in the flat above his office. But again it's just me here in this flat, calling friends I could rely on. I was there two nights and then he had to go back to Berlin. I went back to Hamburg, and I'm not sure how I survived the weekend.

By this time, I had found a forum for neuro Lyme and managed to write in. I wrote:

This is an emergency. I'm in Hamburg. I think I may have neuroborreliosis, please, I don't have much longer.

Then, a woman shared and came back with five recommendations for a doctor locally. I called the first one, they had a waiting list. I couldn't afford to wait two more months, so I called the next one on the list, a GP. They immediately rang the specialist and persuaded them to take me on an emergency basis.

I did notice a change in my brain from the meds the doctor was giving me, but it wasn't enough to be sustainable. I called my friend and was like, you have to come with me. I cannot sit through any more of these doctor's appointments trying to argue my case. He came with me, and I'm afraid that when you have a man who is calm and advocating for you, things happen.

We went straight there, and I will never forget the situation. We got there, and I was trying to speak, but by that time it was nearly impossible. I managed to get out as much as I could and the doctor just said, "You've not told me anything I've not heard before."

I thought, "Thank goodness, finally someone who will listen to me!"

At first glance, he said it would be best to put me in an artificial coma for three months, but logistically we couldn't do that. So instead, I was taking all of these antibiotics at once. After a month, we tried to stop and start again to give my body a rest. We tried to have a few IV days per week instead of full-on treatments, but I was back to day one with symptoms, so we had to start a different regime.

I was home for four or five months. In May 2008, I went back to work. I went to the doctor on Monday, Wednesday, and Friday for my drink and was still taking oral antibiotics at home. He did his absolute best, and he's been punished by the system and the state for what he did, which is tragic. I think he's given up now because of everything that happened.

But anyway, we aren't there yet. Over time, we worked on reducing treatments as we could and finding a way to improve as much as possible with as little as possible. Finally, around August 2010 I started to feel good. I was at like 95%, and thought I was good. I asked if we could stop treatments because I wanted to celebrate.

I booked my dream holiday, which was going on a cycle tour and backpacking through Vietnam, Cambodia, and Thailand. It was also going to be my 50th birthday, and when I checked the itinerary, I was scheduled to be at Angkor Wat. How cool is that—I'm going to spend my 50th at Angkor Wat!

On that day, we got up, we rode there and watched the sunrise. Then I heard this voice, so I turned around. Someone was saying, "Kathryn, is that you?"

And now I have to believe in something because this was a woman that I had been a patient with in a little surgery getting IV therapy. We laid there on the drip tables, talking, encouraging each other that someday things would be better. Then, there she was at Angkor Wat. It was a weird experience, but amazing.

Then, in December 2010, it all came back.

I started getting pains in the left side of my abdomen. I went to the doctor and they couldn't find anything. It kept on and was getting worse, so I went to the doctor who had given me the vaccine to go to Asia and they couldn't find anything. I thought maybe I'd caught some tropical disease. But I thought, at least I'm home. Then, it comes to the point where the whole of my torso feels like it is full of barbed wire.

In desperation, I went back to the Lyme doctor because I didn't know where else to go. He was actually on holiday so the locum just took blood and did the standard test for Lyme disease. When I got back to get the results a week later, my Lyme doctor was back and he just said very calmly, "This is the Lyme disease."

I remember sitting on his bench and feeling my jaw physically drop because I thought this was all behind me. And I was like, okay, so we need to start again. So we started again. I had another year and a half of weekly antibiotic drips and oral antibiotics, and just kind of figured this was going to be my life.

Then, in 2013, they said I had hip dysplasia from birth, so I needed a hip replacement. In February 2013, I had a hip replacement. In October 2013, I went on holiday in Israel. I lost my phone. I was having difficulty packing my suitcase. I started to wonder if it was coming back again. I went to the doctor when I got home and he said it might just be residual viruses in my brain, so I took some antivirals.

It was also getting harder for him at this time because he was getting so much pressure from the system that he was trying to move into private practice. But, he always listened to my concerns and made me feel validated. It got really bad in January 2014. My brain was filled with pressure and weird sensations.

I went to the Army hospital because I didn't want to go back to the other hospital and risk getting sent back to psychiatry. Again, they did all the tests and couldn't find anything. And again, they're starting to say, maybe this could be a mental health issue and I was starting to think, "Oh no, not again."

I was there for a week, and then I left. I kept seeing my doctor and took some more antibiotics, but nothing helped. In October 2014, it got to a point that my body completely collapsed. I hadn't been protecting the gut, I hadn't been doing the detoxes that we know now are helpful. I was still trying to live a normal life, at the time I was in France on an educational holiday. I was ill there so I had to go to the doctor and try to explain in French what was wrong.

I had a boyfriend at the time, and we went to Brussels for the weekend and I ended up in emergency. It was awful. I was trying to explain in Brussels what was going and trying to text with the Lyme doctor here, it was a nightmare. I was living from hour to hour because the pain was so horrendous. I haven't worked since October 2014.

It's only been in recent months that I've gotten the pain levels under a reasonable level on a scale of 10. During that time, I tried so many things. I went to Munich, but that wasn't any help. I went to a neurologist who was supposed to be an expert, and he didn't really help because the drips and the other treatments didn't work for me. It was then that I realized I needed to build up the gut.

I thought my diet was good. But then I learned about oxalates, which were agitating my gut and creating these sharp crystals. My daily pain level was seven to 10, every day. I was glad that I could sleep because that was the only time I wasn't in this severe pain. I found this group that helped me learn more about it, but when I tried to bring it up with a doctor, they kind of dismissed it.

There's a clinic in England that does fecal material trans-plantation, which is a procedure designed to restore the gut biome by relocating it in the body. I decided to go there and have this done. I told my elder sister that I was going to come over for this procedure. She and my brother-in-law came down while I was there doing these two weeks of treatment. I feel like to do this treatment you have to be really desperate because it sounds so gross.

Unfortunately, it didn't work. It changes your immune system. Viruses are usually in check, but when you do this, it throws off the balance. And my brain fog started getting worse and worse. I felt the paralysis coming on again. I actually went back to the university hospital that put me in psychiatry in 2007, being the trusting person that I was, thinking by 2015 surely they would have better doctors and treatments.

Again, I'm on the floor in emergency, trying to explain what's going on. They asked if I'd been there before, and I said yes. The doctor asked to look in the archives. I said that was fine, but that was before my Lyme diagnosis and I'm a known Lyme patient. I have had treatment since that point.

And they just look at me like I'm crazy. And put me right back into psychiatry. This time, they had a room at the hospital so they just kept me there, but back in I went. It was like Groundhog Day.

I actually sent blood to Armin Blesch, who has a specialty laboratory for tickborne diseases in Bavaria. When the blood results came back and I showed them to the psychiatrist, Armin Blesch actually rang the psychiatrist on the ward and said, "I have this patient's blood and we've analyzed it and she's got Epstein bar values that we rarely see because they're so high. She has a whole range of viruses and there is also still evidence of borrelia."

Then I got mail from Armin that based on his conversation, it was clear that the psychiatrist didn't have any knowledge of pathogens and the human body. I still had to wait for the paralysis to go and in the meantime, I had to keep taking whatever antipsychotic medications they were trying to give me and do all these ridiculous surveys.

I actually started taping the conversations, which they got really annoyed about. I knew that I had that right, though. I wanted to make sure that I knew what was being said. I still have the tapes today, but I can't listen to them. It's hard enough remembering it, being surrounded by all these white coats, asking you questions and trying to push me into their treatments and suggestions.

I called the ombudsman and asked, but they just sat on the fence and didn't do anything. I got out after a week, and again they made me sign something to leave. I couldn't walk, couldn't really function well. I went back to the Lyme doctor, who is now private. He did his best. He tried to give me morphine, and that didn't work. Even having clothing on my skin was too much. I was in so much horrific pain.

There was a doctor from a clinic that was supposed to be an expert, so I made an appointment thinking he would help, but nothing came of it. I couldn't pay the private doctor anymore, so I went to a Lyme doctor in the next state over and he tried to treat me again with antibiotics and a lot of supplements, then it gets to March 2018. I have double hip dysplasia. I had one done but I needed to get the second one done and it was fantastic. I got three weeks in hospital and then you get three weeks on the coast in a rehab facility and it worked out great, but that's because a hip replacement is standard and Lyme disease isn't.

I was also part of Lyme UK, and they wanted to be repre-sented at an event in Prague, so I went to Prague on their behalf and spoke to all these people, meanwhile in all this pain and feeling terrible.

In 2016, I was like this isn't the life I wanted. I'm in this B&B all alone, I can't do anything. I was someone who traveled the world. I have to fix this on my own. So I came to Germany. I said this is okay, I don't want this anymore. I joined Dignitas, which is the assisted suicide organization in Zurich.

I think it was June 2016, I called them and asked if they could send me the instructions for assisted suicide. They were really nice and told me they'd had some people from France with Lyme disease who were just done with it. So I got the documents and I wrote the letter saying, this is what I want. It's complicated, though, because you need reports and there's not many doctors who are going to give you those reports if they know what you're going to use them for.

It is also expensive and you need someone to travel with you. I contacted places in the Netherlands because it costs less, but they still had to look into your situation and you have to spend the money and it's not guaranteed. People thought it was extreme but I will tell you, I don't want to die. This isn't about living or dying. It's about getting out of pain. But that obviously didn't happen.

How many doctors did you see before you found your final doctor and got your diagnosis?

I saw tons of doctors, psychiatrists, and others. I can't even remember a number. I ended up the emergency room a lot, so I saw all kinds of doctors and medical people.

What was your official diagnosis from testing?

The results in psychiatry were positive for IGM. Another test said "borderline." A Lyme doctor would say you have a positive result. The psychiatrist, who doesn't know about Lyme disease, took a highlighter and marked it and said, look, this is a negative result.

I also had a lumbar puncture because to prove that you have neuroborreliosis, you need a positive lumbar puncture. Lyme-literate doctors know that's not an effective measurement, but they believe that this is indicative of Lyme in the brain.

What treatments did you use?

I was on antibiotics for three years, including oral and IV drips, from 2007 to 2010. It took a while to find a good routine. I started back to work a few hours a week and by May 2008 I was working mostly full time. But in 2010, it got bad again and I had to start all over again.

When I got to age 60, disulfiram was the "new kid on the block." I had to buy it from someone who got it from Poland where it's sold over the counter. At the same time, I thought to myself that if this didn't work, then I was done. After a year, it's much improved and it gives me a lot of hope.

I actually got lucky because I met Janey, who is so big in the community and her story is so similar to mine. She said, get out of there and go to see Dr. Lambert in Dublin. I said, "I don't have the money."

She told me there was a Lyme treatment fund and that she would write me a recommendation. I also got a neighbor to write a recommendation and then I applied, and they paid for me to go to Dublin to see Dr. Lambert.

What was your family relationship like?

Considering that I'm in Germany and the family is in England, I just have such a different life from them. There wasn't really a great amount of contact before Lyme, just because our lives grew apart. I did try to call an elder sister in 2007 and explain what was happening. I told her I felt like I had early Alzheimer's. And then when I told her I had Lyme, she reacted really angrily, so I just figured I had no support. I always had James. He was always at the end of the phone. He was phenomenal.

What do you think about the future of Lyme disease? Are you hopeful there's a cure?

Now that I'm with Dr. Lambert and I've made great progress, I feel much more optimistic. There are people wanting to research this. We just have to break through that wall of getting the mainstream to listen. I don't think it's like it was before where we didn't have enough knowledge. I think we have plenty of knowledge, yes we can use more, but there's enough to get doctors started.

My hope is that it will happen and we will break through. We just need maybe one good push to get things rolling.

What message, last piece of advice, or words of encouragement would you like to provide to the Lyme community?

Don't give up. Believe in yourself.

Three Important Reminders:

1. You Matter.

2. You Are Loved.

3. Everything WILL be Okay.

LAURA NUNEZ

Nice, France

Connected

Optimistic

Real

Laura lives in Nice, France, and has been through quite a journey in her lifetime. As an educator and counselor, she was smart enough to do her research and reach out, demanding that people provide the help and support that she needs. She has always been optimistic, which helped her through the worst times. Today, she's still working on her treatment and connecting with the community to help others, too.

What are three words that describe you?

Connected, optimistic, and real.

Do you have a song that inspired you through this journey?

Not one in particular, but music is huge in general. It varies based on the mood as to what I listen to, but all music has been a big part of my life.

Where did your journey begin?

I grew up near Chicago in the Western suburbs. We lived in Downers Grove and then we moved to a town called Oak Brook and while I was in high school, my family moved to the upper peninsula of Michigan. I can't be sure, but I did grow up with a dog and I remember my mom pulling ticks off him. And when I was really young, I remember having some joint pain behind my knees. My parents always used to call them "growing pains."

They took me to doctors, I got blood tests, and there was just never any answer. I guess they just went away on their own. But the other thing that was weird was that my father was a doctor and he diagnosed me when I was only 11 years old with goiter, and basically they confirmed I was hypothyroid. That's another thing I look back and say, was that normal? But other than that, I didn't have anything weird. I wasn't sick more than other people, I didn't have allergies, there is nothing else I could think of. Everything was normal, I went to university in Ann Arbor, and lived there for eight years. Then, I did some study abroad for a master's in teaching.

My parents were big travelers. They took us to Europe several times. My father is Mexican, so we went back to Mexico for Christmas every year for like, 10 years. So, it was natural for me to be curious and wanting to travel. When I first got my teaching degree, I was in my twenties. I got a job in Mexico and moved there and taught for three years. I got some normal bugs like everyone does in Mexico—I don't think you can avoid that. But again, it didn't strike me as anything weird.

After the job in Mexico, I moved back to the states and re-located to San Francisco. I lived there for almost a decade. I was teaching, I went back and got another master's degree in counseling to work as an advisor at the college level. I worked at a public school in San Francisco, too, but then the travel bug started itching again, so I went to another travel job fair.

I said to myself, "If someone offers me a job in Italy, there's no way I can say no."

And I was offered a job in Italy, in Milan.

I ended up teaching in Milan for two years. When my contract was up and I really wanted to move back to San Francisco, that was also when the major recession hit in 2008. I was desperate to go back to the Bay area, but people were hesitant to do online interviews, that wasn't really a thing then. They wanted me to fly back for interviews and I tried a few times, but it wasn't sustainable to be doing that all the time.

So, I had a friend who was also stuck in Milan in the summer, and she suggested we take a trip. I said, okay, let's go to Paris. We can rent an Airbnb, have a good time. We went, and it was one of those things that as soon as we arrived, I was like, this is where I need to be. I moved to Paris and lived there illegally for a while. I was doing some underground work as a nanny, tutoring, cleaning, stuff like that. I was having the time of my life, looking for a job at the same time.

I had also started seeing someone, so things were all kind of coming together. I ended up being able to move back to San Francisco and at the same time, I got a job offer in Barcelona, so I moved to Barcelona. I taught there for five years, but the pay was quite low. I loved the city and the school and the kids, but I decided to see if I could move up the ladder. I was then hired as a university social/emotional counselor in Prague, Czech Republic.

I moved to Prague and the school was probably the second-best school I've taught at in my entire life. The school, the teachers, the kids—it was all really top-notch. My first year was good. One of the things that was really intense for me, though, is that even though I have a master's in counseling, California is very particular about the program. You have to choose from one of six concentrations, and I remember saying to myself, "I don't want to be a therapist because I can't handle that level of emotional burden." So, I worked with kids and did what I could until there was a point where I would refer them out if necessary. But in Prague, I ended up doing so much therapeutic counseling that I just felt I was starting to absorb it. That's why I didn't become an FMT (functional medicine therapist)—not only is it too heavy for me, but I don't feel qualified to help someone who has these serious mental health issues.

In the international teaching world, you have to tell them very early on whether you're going to come back the following year. You have to notify them in October whether you will be returning for the following school year. That's a huge window of time where so many things can happen. But they need to know so that they can go recruiting other teachers that they need.

I remember having the paper, and everything in my body told me not to re-sign for another year, but I did. That was a turning point. It was 2015, and I flew to the U.S. for the Christmas holidays. I had already traveled to like 45 countries. I had been to so many places, and every holiday I had I was traveling. I was a maniac, constantly on the go.

I came back from another one of my power trips where I was in New York and San Francisco. Then I got back, and I was at work, and I remember feeling this weird cool sensation on the back of my neck. Then, I had this sensation that I had to put my head between my knees so that the blood would come back into my head. This happened a few times, and then I think I went to the emergency room and nothing really came of it.

I remember sitting in a meeting at another point and people were talking about something and I got really anxious. I was thinking, "Oh my god, are they thinking I'm not doing my job right?"

I was so anxious about my performance, and then it just seeped out to every part of my life. I had serious generalized anxiety all of a sudden, to the extent that I was worried I might just die in the night. I also had heart palpitations, and I remember that I would try to sleep, but I couldn't sleep on my left side because my heart was pounding and the noise was keeping me awake.

I went to the clinic, and they ran some tests. I think the only thing they found was that my thyroid, my TSH, was a little bit off. I went back and they had me wear a heart monitor, I saw a cardiologist, and all of that came back normal. I got a little frustrated with that clinic, so I asked my colleagues for another referral. At that second clinic, the doctor put me on some beta blockers, which make your heart slow down.

I also remember him asking me, "Are you sure you're not anxious because, you know, you're 45 and you're not married, and you don't have kids?"

I remember thinking, well, maybe, but that doesn't describe all the things that are going on. I went home for the summer, and I felt better. I was doing college tours and staying with my mom. When I wasn't working, I felt better. I got back to school in the fall, and it all started back up again.

I felt like I was having a nervous breakdown. I told my boss, I'm sorry but I can't come back. Everything in my body is saying I can't come back. He told me to take my time, he said he wasn't going to hire anyone over the holidays to replace me. He was like, "You're the best counselor I've ever worked with."

And I really appreciated that, but this job felt like it was literally killing me. Like, I felt like if I stayed it would just keep getting worse. But I took the holiday to think about it anyway. I didn't change my mind, though. I knew I had to go. At that point, I knew that I had to change jobs, and I had gotten an interview at the International School of Monaco. Then, I came back from break, and it's another one of those moments I'll never forget. I started feeling pins and needles in my left foot.

After a few days, I started feeling pins and needles in my right foot.

Then, I started feeling pins and needles in both my hands.

Then I developed numbness patches on both my hands.

It just kept accelerating until the end of the school year in June. I was able to finish out the school year, but by then, my legs, my torso, and even my face were having issues with numbness and tingling. So, I paid for COBRA because I had a pretty good insurance package and I could afford it, and I went home to stay with my mom.

What was your journey to a diagnosis like?

My mom was living in Chicago again, in the suburbs. I went to see her GP, who did some tests, but nothing came of that. She suggested that I go see a neurologist. Thank God my mom knew someone in a hospital in Peoria because the wait list was really long otherwise. We went down there to see the neurologist and he did an MRI, some basic reflex and vibration testing. Basically, he said that I had some loss of sensation in my feet, but there was really no specific cause or reason for it.

The one thing he did say that made me feel better is that it definitely wasn't MS. At this point, I'd started to worry that it was something like MS, Lou Gehrig's, or what have you, so that was a bit of a relief.

That was June 2017, and by August, I was walking with a cane. As I'm heading off to Monaco for my new job, I'm just thinking, God let me get on the plane and get to this place so that I can get healthcare again. My COBRA was ending, and I didn't have a job. I made it on the plane, and I got signed up for healthcare and I saw a whole slew of doctors.

I saw a generalist who did bloodwork, but that was nothing. Another theory was a loss of B12, so I saw a specialist for B12 injections, but that didn't really do much. Then, finally, in October, I saw a neurologist and he did some tests, including the one where they hook you up and shock different parts of your body, I forget what it's called in English. That showed that I had severe carpal tunnel in both hands and that my peroneal nerve on both sides was severely damaged.

I was so relieved that there was something—there was a physical test result that showed that something was actually wrong with me. He sent me to the head internist at the hospital in Monaco, who admitted me to the hospital and did a lot of tests. He did blood tests, a spinal tap, and tons of other tests. I went back and saw him and he said, "Look, you've got some type of immunodeficient/neurodegenerative disease. I'm not sure what it is right now, but I'm going to give you a treatment and we'll see if it works."

When he suggested that I get the immunoglobulin treatment, I did my research and figured, why not give it a try? This was the IVIG treatment. They did three loading doses, for which they would admit me for a week. I was in the hospital for a week in November, then December, and then in January. I think they only had a half round for the third round, but I still was admitted for the full week.

My French is okay, but not good enough for medical emergencies. It was very confusing to me because it didn't feel like anyone was explaining to me what was going on. I remember one time, when the doctor was coming around, I asked, "Well, what's the diagnosis?"

He said, "We can't do that here. You're going to have to go to a specialist center."

I thought, well, what the hell, isn't this the place I should be? But I left, and when I went back to the neurologist, he asked what happened at the hospital.

"What do you mean, what happened?"

"Well, the doctor said that you were questioning him and his treatment or that you didn't have faith in him and his ability to treat you. He doesn't really think he wants to see you again."

I told him I had merely asked about a diagnosis, and he said, "Well, I don't think it's a good idea for you to go back there."

I said, okay, so where do I go? He referred me to go to the main hospital in Nice. I'm not sure if I went right away. I can't remember. I do remember that after I got the first round of IVIG, my hands started to feel better. I was getting better, but very incrementally. There were little, slow improvements, and by the next summer, I didn't need the cane to walk all the time.

I still had vasculitis, brain fog, tinnitus, probably all sorts of other weird things I can't remember. However, it had gotten to be more manageable. I remember my first year of work here, it took everything just to get on the train and make it to work and then get on the train and go back home. Then, I would just be on my couch trying to recover enough for the next day. I also had a lot of dizziness, so that made things a challenge.

But my students and the work that I do kept me going. Then, it's the summer of 2018 and I went back home, and once again, when I stop working, I start feeling better. Now, obviously, I understand that's because I was resting and giving my body what it needed. I wasn't stressed, I was sleeping, there was nothing to exacerbate it.

At this point, I'm in this mentality of having this illness and not knowing what it will do or what kind of life I will have. I kind of feel like I'm in this "final" place so I decided that I wanted to go on one more date and have one last fling. So I go on a date, and I'm thinking this guy is cute enough, he'll work for my last fling. After that, I was like, closing up the shop and was just going to be done.

However, it ended up being more than a fling, and we actually started seeing each other some more. Once again, this was another turning point, there was something in that relationship that caused me stress. This was in about February of 2019, and I remember thinking, I'm still not okay. Symptoms were popping back up and although I was a lot better, I still wasn't okay.

I went and found another neurologist and she handed me the same paperwork with the same blood tests. Then, I got a call from the lab in March of 2019, and they told me, "You tested positive for Lyme disease."

I was looking back after this, and I had all these notes and I had "Lyme " in the notes with a big question mark. I was relieved in a sense that I finally had an answer, but I was not relieved because I had done my research and knew that Lyme was not an easy disease or diagnosis.

How many doctors did you see before reaching your official diagnosis?

I don't know exactly how many practitioners I saw over the years, but it was a lot. I saw GPs, specialists, and all kinds of emergency doctors, and none of them figured it out until the last doctor did.

What was the treatment journey like?

Once I had my diagnosis, I decided to go back to the hospital in Nice and see an infectious disease doctor. She gave me doxycycline for two weeks. I didn't know it at the time, but I had a massive HERCs. I was so out of it. I was watching a movie with my boyfriend, and I couldn't even tell you what the movie was about. I couldn't concentrate at all. I couldn't get off the couch.

I stopped the doxy myself because I felt so sick. I had to go to the emergency room twice because I had a UTI, so it wasn't working. I went back to her and she said that the only other thing we could do is to put in a PICC line. That, however, seemed really dangerous and drastic to me. There were so many things that could go wrong. I decided that wasn't the way I wanted to go.

That's when I started doing more research and found

Stephen Buhner and I started doing some self-treating. I went down the rabbit hole of all the different treatments and options out there to try and figure out what to do from there.

At this time, I also found a woman working in a small town in France. This was pre-COVID. I took the train to see her, and she immediately looked at my tongue and told me I had something I can't even pronounce or spell. I told her that my stomach was always upset and felt like it was full of acid, it's always burning.

She had her own way of treating, she didn't follow Buhner or believe in anything he did. She called it endogenic medicine, I think, modeled after another French person that started it. So she mixed me up a batch of herbs and sent me on my way. I left again for the States and took the herbs with me, but I didn't really like the interaction with her. She seemed to have a chip on her shoulder and we didn't click, so I looked for another doctor when I got home.

I found a doctor in England, thanks to the UK Lyme group. She was doing muscle testing, which at the time was relatively unheard of. She did that with me and gave me a five-page handout. I had to order all of this stuff from all of these companies, and then COVID hit. I couldn't order anything, things weren't going to get delivered. I knew the only thing I could get were my herbs, so I decided just to go back to those in the meantime.

During COVID, I was doing my herbs. It was tough. The doxy destroyed my stomach. Then I had major urinary issues, they did more tests, and it kept on. Then, finally, we got through the worst of COVID, and I decided to go visit my mom and see a doctor near her. I found a nurse practitioner who specializes in Lyme and saw her in May of 2021.

She did things like the Geneva diagnostic test and other things that had never been done. She was also the one that realized that I didn't actually have a urinary tract infection or anything. The bacteria had moved south and colonized my urinary tract, as well. She got me on all these probiotics and that helped clear it up. I told her that I had such a bad time with antibiotics, and since my gut was in such bad shape, she let me stick with herbs for the time being.

It's interesting, though, because in the meantime, I was doing baseline testing with the neurologist to see what was working and what wasn't. Things weren't getting worse and the nerve conduction test had actually improved after herbal treatment. My body is almost 100% quiet now. The main challenge is trying to get what she recommends. It's difficult to get the peptides and everything you need. I try to load up when I'm in the U.S., but sometimes I'm left scrambling to find someone, usually from the UK, who can send me stuff.

I think living overseas has delayed my treatment a little bit because it's harder to get a hold of things. If I were living in the U.S. with my mother, I think it would have been much quicker and I wouldn't have to have this "stop, go" type of treatment.

How has Lyme impacted your life?

Lyme has made me a completely different person. I used to take such pleasure in traveling. I took an entire year out of my life and backpacked through the Middle East, North Africa, and had the time of my life. I identified as the person who was traveling to find herself and explore the world. To me, this meant that I was in line with the universe and I would meet people along my journey. Because I don't travel as much anymore, that has shrunk significantly.

I feel really lucky that I'm still able to work, because I know many people can't. I relate more to others who are suffering. I think more too about others and invisible illnesses, and it has made me more empathic. I used to think more materialistic, but those things don't mean as much to me anymore. The people who actually still stay by your side through this—that's another huge impact. Some people can't deal with the way Lyme debilitates you and you lose a lot of people along the journey.

Has Lyme impacted your career or career goals at all?

It kind of made me rethink my own success and what I consider success. When I was working in Prague at that fantastic job, my body gave out entirely. So that was kind of an indicator that I wasn't going to be able to do this. It's interesting, in the past year, I've been revalidating myself. Before, I was telling myself I was lucky to have a job, and I tried to keep my head down so I didn't get noticed for anything negative.

But then, I started to realize that I'm doing okay. I've grown as a professional because I know what I'm doing, but I've also grown as a person. I recently applied to be on a committee with my professional organization and I was a mentor with another educator this year. The Lyme community has made me want to be more connected to my professional community if that makes sense.

Has Lyme impacted friendships, family, relationships, etc.?

My mother and I have always had a really difficult relationship, or we did up until I started suffering from Lyme symptoms. Since then, she's been fully supportive and helpful through it all and I think it's brought us a lot closer, so I'm grateful for that. I thank her every time I see her because there's no way I would've made it through without her. On the other hand, I lost my brother. I don't think he really understands the ups and downs of the disease. He has certain expectations on our relationship, and the one thing that anyone with Lyme knows is that all that goes right out the window.

I'm lucky that I have some very good friends who just take me as I am, you know. My father had already passed away so I don't know how it would have affected our relationship. I think it would have frustrated him seeing me suffer and having no answers.

It's interesting when you talk about synchronicity. There were two really unique things when I arrived at the school in Monaco. The first is that there was another teacher there whose father had Lyme. The second was meeting a student with another unique Lyme connection. I can't go into the particulars of it here because of privacy and such, but suffice it to say, I could see the universe connecting me to these people. For me, meeting these people really validated the legitimacy of the disease.

Have you found any friends or support along the way?

I joined a group a while back called Lyme Naturally and another called A Right to Heal, as I wanted to give back to the community and help others. There's one woman in particular, from Tick Boot Camp, who I've been following on Instagram. I reached out to her because I was cleaning things out and had all these herbs I wasn't using anymore so I wanted to see if she needed them.

The "great thing" about France is that everyone follows the socialized medicine model, right? However, the thing about socialized medicine is that if you want to go outside of it, you have to pay for it out of your own pocket. And she had no money to buy the herbs and supplements that she needed. I see her continually doing these treatments that I can't imagine—I'd probably be on the floor. But she can't afford to buy herbs or the other stuff and that really breaks my heart.

Where are you at today in your journey?

I feel like I'm at about 80%. I think what people don't talk about is that Lyme doesn't go away. I believe that I will never not have Lyme. I think it takes a lot of time and energy to do the healing, to do the things I need to do. I've been toying with the idea of going part-time at work because I feel like I don't have enough time to take care of myself and my Lyme.

I think if I had more time, I would inch my healing further, but also because it's taken so long to get my gut back in shape, I feel like I'm turning a corner and I feel like it might be time to hit the bacteria again a bit. I think I can maybe get to 90% with that.

What current treatments, routines, and health practices do you have?

I do still take herbs and supplements as I can get ahold of them. I just started taking BPC peptide and within like, two weeks, it made a 100% difference. It's still hard for me because I can't just go like I used to. I have to think about travel time, recovery time, and so forth. I flew back to see my mom and it took me an entire week to recover from the jet lag.

That's not normal, I don't think. So, living with things like that is hard. As I said, I don't have as much time as I'd like to put toward my Lyme self-care, but I am actively treating it and trying to improve as much as I can. I was one of those people who was not ready to change my diet right away because I loved food, but I definitely saw some major differences when I finally did. I try to manage my stress as best I can.

Sleep is huge for me. Moving. I think moving also saved my life. I think even in the worst of it, using the cane, I would force myself to do basic yoga. I believe that had a huge impact. And this peptide I mentioned, wow. It's really been amazing. I think the IVIG gave my immune system the kick that it needed, too.

When you think about the future of Lyme patients, are you hopeful there is a cure?

I am very hopeful. I love listening to podcasts, the Tick Boot Camp and Bay Area Lyme Foundation. I think most recently there was one where they were talking to a scientist and she said there's all these scientists applying for research grants, I'm constantly seeing them on my Instagram, and it comes in droves.

I also think that the more people that mobilize and speak out, the more research will be put into it to find the solutions in the first place. I think that eventually they'll find a cure. I don't know if it will be in my lifetime, and I don't know if it will be a pill or a vaccine or what, but I believe there will be something that will make it easier to live with Lyme, if not to get rid of it entirely.

Any words of advice , encouragement that you would like to offer the rest of the Lyme community?

I think I really doubted myself for a long time. I was hesitant to get support, mostly emotionally. I just kind of accepted a lot of the things. I started thinking about it like six months ago, and I was like, "No, you have a right to get help, and a right to feel better."

I started joining groups and going to those events. I thought, okay, I'm a part of this community, I might as well engage, and they are so welcoming.

Embrace the community.

And most importantly, keep trying. Keep fighting. Trust your body. You know it better than anybody.

BIANCA MICHELE

Sydney, Australia

Ever-Evolving

Creative

Healing

Bianca is an Australian national living in Poland. Her experience with Lyme was quite unlike many that we've seen this far. She was fortunate to get a quick diagnosis, but her treatment dragged on for more than six years and took a lot of overcoming obstacles to get to where she is today. Australia is notorious for ignoring Lyme and actually penalizing doctors for treating it or prescribing related medications, so her story is especially appreciated as part of this book.

What are three words that describe you?

I found this very difficult, to be honest with you. I feel like with Lyme, I was so labeled and boxed in that I've let go of every label and am ever evolving. I would say creative, and always healing.

Do you have a song that inspired you through this journey?

Avril Lavigne wrote a song about Lyme called "Head Above Water" and I really, really loved that song.

Where did your Lyme journey begin?

I was around age 22 at the time. I was starting a lingerie business and just leaving real estate. I thought I was going to do well in real estate but then it just went downhill when everything started happening. I was in Australia and had just started the business, but I started to experience all kinds of symptoms.

It's hard to pinpoint, but I would say that it started with needing a lot of rest. I would need to sleep long amounts of hours yet just never felt rested. I had extreme dissociation and brain fog. I had deep neck headaches and nausea, body aches, stuff like that. And it all seemed to show up pretty much overnight.

I just remember looking in the mirror one day and just not recognizing myself. My face was full of cystic acne and just, yeah, it wasn't me. Not being able to recognize myself and not being able to explain what I was feeling and experiencing was hard, due to the dissociation we refer to as brain fog.

The fatigue was kind of a slow onset, but then everything just kind of came on very quickly and added up, piling up in the blink of an eye. I find it really hard to understand where I was even at. I was in my body, but it wasn't connected.

At one stage, I lost all feeling in my right leg. I woke up one day with what felt like pins and needles and couldn't feel my leg. Eventually, ozone injections helped that. I had to learn to walk again, though, and the doctors didn't know what was wrong. Of course, in Australia, it was denied that I had Lyme. Daily exercise has helped, in addition to ozone therapy, but the doctors still say it was a "mystery" occurrence.

It was only about eight months later, which I know is a very lucky thing, that I got my diagnosis. I had seen a handful of doctors, I couldn't tell you how many, over and over again being told it was nothing to worry about because my bloods was normal. I was misdiagnosed with multiple sclerosis, fibromyalgia, all of these things that didn't actually have a root cause, and I still wasn't getting any answers.

There were no indications in my brain that I had MS. They couldn't pinpoint why I had fibromyalgia if that was it.

Then, it was depression, and even hypochondria from some of them, which led to its own creation of anxiety and depression because the medical community wasn't listening or believing me. Then I told a friend, and this is the most goosebump-inducing experience.

After a really long time of denying it even to myself and to everyone around me, I finally started accepting it and opening up, and I told this friend of mine what had been going on. He reminded me of this time when I was with his mom and we were having dinner and she told this story of her son's friend who had to fly over to Malaysia to have hyperthermia treatment and no one in Australia believed him. She had told me this story about a year earlier and I remember at the time thinking it was horrible, but not really understanding what it really meant.

So, naturally, I was curious now about what this person had. My friend's response was that all the symptoms I'm experiencing were similar to the friend's, and that they sound like Lyme disease. I had no idea what that was. He told me I had to do a specific Lyme disease test and that Germany was the best place to get it done. I actually ordered my tests online. It's such an odd thing, but I wanted any answer possible.

I had the test sent to me and it was all very controlled, with specific requirements for processing. This is really outside of what normally happens, but luckily, the pathology lab I took it to didn't ask a lot of questions. I showed her the instructions on how to do it and she took my blood and I sent it over to Germany.

Within this period of time, they picked the blood back up and within a couple of weeks, I received an email with the Western positive bands, with a really low CD47. I had a positive for borrelia burgdorferi. I was relieved at that moment because I had an answer, but I didn't realize what was actually ahead. I didn't have a Lyme doctor; we didn't know of any at the time. The friend of a friend didn't have a Lyme doctor either, they just knew to try hyperthermia.

What was the treatment journey like?

My story is probably a little different from other people because I went straight to Malaysia. As I mentioned, it was either Malaysia or Germany, in my mind, and this person had such a good experience in Malaysia that it seemed better. He actually healed straightaway by doing that. He went over there and had two hypothermia treatments and was fine. I went over Christmas; I think it was in 2017. I flew to Malaysia and went to the clinic he had attended.

When I arrived in Malaysia at this clinic, I opened the doors and here are people from all countries sitting in recliners with drips in their arms, in the middle of Asia. It was really shocking, to say the least. I had two hyperthermia treatments while I was there and that did help some of the symptoms. From what I've learned, I think it's good that I didn't start taking oral antibiotics right away because that can be difficult on the body.

The process involves one day of vitamin drips, and then one day of hyperthermic treatment. During the hyperthermic treatment, you're under anesthesia and then your body is heated up and essentially forced into a fever. Then, you're given really strong antibiotics while you're under. They can also do it while you're awake but that sounded horribly uncomfortable. I believe they discovered this as a treatment for syphilis first.

I did one treatment, and took a two week break, and then went back for the second one. I think it helped, but I don't think it took care of everything. I don't think it targets the coinfections, either, so I was feeling better but still not cured.

Then, overnight, I was instantly feeling terrible again. Fortunately, in Malaysia, I met a lot of people in the Lyme community who had been sick for years. A lot of them were in wheelchairs and dealing with the worst of the worst cases of Lyme. So they gave me some good Lyme-literate doctors in Australia. I got an appointment with one of them and ended up going on oral antibiotics for a six-month period. That actually turned out to be a bad idea, because it took a serious toll on my gut and got me feeling terrible again in other ways.

I think the next thing I went onto was herbal remedies. I used the Dr. Buhner protocol. I love his methods and herbs, even just for regular colds and viruses. Then, I started to try other things, like ozone therapy. I traveled to Bali to get ozone therapy initially. Funnily enough, my family was planning a vacation and asked if I'd like to go along. Since I'd heard about this clinic in Bali from the Lyme community, I decided to go and do treatments while everyone else was vacationing.

I went to the Philippines for ozone, too, because it's much more affordable. I could get one in Australia for the price of 20 in Asia, so I always traveled when I could to save the money. Even getting flights and hotels was cheaper than having it done, in most cases. This went on for six years, I should mention, and after all of these treatments I still wasn't feeling well. I started to notice the community talking about CIRS (Chronic Inflammatory Response

Syndrome) and mold illness, as well, and I was like, well I'm living in a new property, so I probably don't need to stress about mold. I decided to get my house tested for EMF (electromagnetic fields) because I had this combination of feeling good after treatment and then coming home and feeling terrible again.

The guy that came to do the testing told me that everything was fine and I didn't need to worry about EMF or anything else. A few hours after he left, my phone rang and it was the EMF specialist. He said, "This is going to sound really strange, and I don't know if you're going to believe me anyway, but I have a really high sensitivity to mold and I can't get out of bed after being in your property."

So that opened up the next box and I contacted my doctor and informed him about what was happening. He confirmed that they see this all the time and advised that we have a mold test done on the property. We got a mold test done and he actually did a HLA-DR test that came back positive, saying I had CIRS. Then, the test for mold in my property was outrageous. There were extreme amounts of different types of molds throughout the property.

There are a few areas of thought about this. People say micro toxins can be carried from your car or old belongings. There are some instances where new properties just aren't built right and there's a water leak or something else that allows mold to develop. There are so many potential ways that mold can get into "new" construction that even homes less than five years old aren't safe from potential dangers.

I never really found the exact source in that property, but it was dangerously high. I had to move out of the mold first and foremost. The suggestion was to actually get rid of everything. It's really extreme, but the micro toxins make it dangerous to keep anything. I decided to go ahead and do that and went and stayed with my parents for a little bit. But I realized I wasn't feeling well there either. I would leave the house and notice that I felt better, but then going indoors and feeling worse.

I was really starting to notice that sensitivity to mold, but it also feels so much like Lyme that it was hard to tell. I realized there was mold at their house and ended up moving into a tent in their backyard to remove myself entirely. It was one of the best things I did because I started feeling much better. I still had all the symptoms here and there like fatigue and the other little Lyme symptoms, but I had a lot of brain fog lifted. Then, it was just a process of fixing all the bloodwork that can be affected.

I had to try and find a new property after a few months, and luckily I did. Right away, I started to experience histamine reactions from the new property. I had bladder pain, red eyes, and a lot of new symptoms. When I contacted my Lyme doctor again, he said that some people are also dealing with mast cell activation syndrome, so from there he suggested I go on disulfiram to get rid of that and stop the borrelia again. That was another six months of disulfiram after that, which is very heavy. It was effective and did work, but it still didn't take care of the whole picture.

It also had an effect on the brain, as well, I had a lot of emotional issues while I was on it. However, I was having glimpses of remission throughout each of these periods even though it wasn't the full picture. I just decided to start detoxing and see if a really good detox protocol could help. It was almost like that was the part that was missing the whole time because I was taking a lot of things in but my detox channels were all blocked, so I wasn't able to eliminate things like I should have.

I also started taking Cistus Tea. Have you heard of that from Klingheart? That was really amazing, it works on bacteria and retroviruses and did wonders. I also started doing bladder cleanses, full body cleanses, and a variety of detoxes. I was also mixing those with the Buhner protocols to supplement with the herbs.

Then, I started traveling to Poland. I have some family from here and it's incredible for Lyme treatment. It's actually one of the best places to come if you have Lyme because the doctors are educated and really supportive. They're active on teaching people how to avoid it and they do a lot of alternative treatments, too. Probably the hardest part is the language barrier, honestly.

I was really skeptical, but I decided to try the Rife machine. In the end, that was really helpful. Everything always helped, I feel that's important to mention. I don't feel like there wasn't anything that was a waste of time or ineffective. The Rife machine was so impressive that I bought my own.

How has Lyme impacted your life?

I feel like it completely broke me to pieces. The way that I explain it the best is that I felt so squeezed from everything I ever was prior to having this. I realize how distant I felt from my true self when I was going through this. I always describe it as the biggest gift. It was like a front row seat into my soul. There was no support, the medical system didn't understand, friends and family weren't willing to understand, and I was left mostly in my room alone. Through that experience, the only way I could really look was within.

I don't know if many people get that opportunity to be in such a low place where they are in need of being saved and realizing that they have been there to save themselves all along. And I was able to see that I was there, all along, and that was all I needed. So yes, Lyme has had a serious impact on my life in several ways, but I have managed to find the positive.

Do you feel like you missed out on anything?

I missed birthdays, weddings, friends' events and activities, all kinds of things. I wasn't able to show up for people, or myself. That left me in a dark place a lot of the time, feeling like I wasn't going to make it. I missed out on a lot and it was extremely difficult to get through.

Have you found any friends or support along the way?

When I was in Malaysia, I met a lady who followed me on Instagram and gave me the idea to make a Lyme-specific Instagram. It has like 10,000 followers now, I think, and it gave us all a chance to connect and help each other out. I would say that it definitely saved my life in many respects. I appreciate all of the Lyme communities that I have found along the way.

When you think about the future of Lyme patients, are you hopeful there is a cure?

I definitely am. I am hopeful that it's an herb or a pharmaceutical that will allow us to really get rid of it from where it starts so it doesn't just stay in the body. But I also think we have to look at all the comorbidities, too, that would be much more effective. I think if we could look at it on a deeper level, we could identify the combination of emotional, physical, and environmental factors that lead to Lyme and its various incarnations.

For me, personally, I found remission by healing my symptoms. I realized that it's also an immune issue because so many people have different Lyme experiences. If we can get there, we can maybe teach bodies how to cope at that deeper level. But I think we need to look at it as a whole picture in order to get there.

How do you feel (or hope) that sharing your story will help?

I think it will help others to believe that it's possible to heal. I think sharing my story helps me now, it's part of my purpose and I can't go back to my old life now. It also helps me to know that there's someone now I can help that is in the position I was in once.

I want to remind others that they can heal, too.

Any words of advice, encouragement, etc. that you'd like to offer the rest of the Lyme community?

I feel like I tried everything from antibiotics to hyperthermia and even disulfiram. It took every piece of me to heal. I want to remind people that even if you're in your bed, in that dark place in the early stages of your experience, this is just the beginning for you. There may not be a cure right now, but there is remission and healing is possible to all. I would just remind them to connect back to their heart

"Courage conquers all things:
it even gives strength to the body."

-Ovid

CHRISTOPHER SPENCER

Darlinghurst, Australia

Honest

Sarcastic

Lighthearted

Chris is located in Darlinghurst, an eastern suburb of Sydney, Australia. He's a New Zealand native, but because of his Lyme disease, he feels like he is limited and must stay in Sydney so he can be close to his doctor.

What are three words that describe you?

I would say honest, sarcastic, and lighthearted.

Do you have a song that inspired you through this journey?

Probably Sia. I like Sia's music in general and it has been helpful in several ways. It's melodic and easy to listen to and she talks about struggles and coming through it in a way that resonates with me.

Where did your journey begin?

I was about 27, and up until that point I was super-active. I was always healthy, never spent much time in hospital or doctors, none of that. Then, it started with an upset stomach and digestive issues. I was having stomach cramps, diarrhea, and related issues. It continued for a couple weeks, and then carried on into a couple of months of these symptoms before others started appearing.

I was seeing multiple doctors at this time. I wasn't very familiar with the medical system so in my mind, you go to the doctor, you get what you need, and you're fine. Additional symptoms popped up, including ulcers and peeling of the roof of my mouth, flu-like symptoms like fatigue, body aches, and so forth.

Over a space of like four months, all this progressed and evolved. The strangest symptom, by far, is that below my knees there's this spot that rubs against pants and becomes painful after a long period. It's symmetrical on both legs and it just creates a lot of skin pain and irritation. It feels like they're on fire and have needles in them.

Through all this, I'm in Australia and my family is still in New Zealand, and I'm not used to being sick or infirm or anything like that. It was kind of very much like, "What's going on?"

What was your journey to a diagnosis like?

I didn't really understand what's happening, so I went to a few local GPs and they were all pretty much the same, suggesting I try this or that with no real results. One GP was more helpful. She went out of her way to run tests and try to help me figure out what was going on. Then I got referrals to a hospital in Sydney known as St. Vincent's, which is the major hospital in the city and it's one of the best.

I went to a gastroenterologist, and she said, "Yes, there's definitely something going on, but we don't know what." So, she did an endoscopy and said that she couldn't really see anything obvious.

"Everything looks fine. I can tell there's something wrong, but honestly, I just don't know what it is."

She pre-ordered a bunch of tests and then I got referred to an immunologist, which took three or four months of waiting. This was stressful because in the meantime, I had no idea what was going on, what the test results were that were just out there waiting, and so on. Plus, it was a lot of chasing down the immunologist to actually get the appointment.

After waiting and thinking that the immunologist would

have answers, being hopeful that there would be something, I walked in and again, everything was "fine."

They did a lot of tests, and throughout all of them, the immunologist couldn't see anything wrong. So of course, I was like, well what now? I'm obviously not well, but no one had any answers.

From there, I was referred to a neurologist, as well as an oral immunologist due to the mouth symptoms, but they also couldn't see anything wrong. The neurologist said that it was probably mechanical allodynia, which literally translates to "other pain." They did tests and scans for MS, including full-body scans and CTs, and nothing of note showed up.

No one was dismissive or anything. Everyone believed me and agreed that something was wrong. They just couldn't determine what it was. The gastroenterologist and the neurologist thought maybe I'd had a virus that I'd gotten over, and these effects were just leftover from that.

I was given antibiotics during this time, which led to common things like fatigue and HERCs and so forth, but Lyme also wasn't even on my radar at this point, so I just assumed I had a really bad infection of some kind and that was the cause of it all.

I started seeing an integrative doctor in 2018, who kind of went through the usual steps. They have wider testing and consider more extensive things, so they explored some different avenues. Even she struggled to work out what it could be. With her, though, Lyme came up.

I was initially dismissive of this because I had the misconception that Lyme includes that bulls-eye rash and since I didn't have that, I didn't figure it could be Lyme. Plus, aside from visiting my grandad on the Gold Coast when I was a kid, I was never anywhere I thought that I could contract Lyme. In reflection, I realize that I should have been more open instead of dismissing it, but we just kind of took it out of the cards and went back to searching.

I also developed really severe headaches that just wouldn't go away in mid-2018. My conception was that you get a headache, you take ibuprofen, and it goes away. Now, I'm living with headaches constantly and nothing will make them go away. The integrative doctor put me on an eight-week program for a general virus/bacteria treatment, which included antibiotics that made me very ill.

I have a tendency to persevere, so I kept going and pushing along, assuming that this would all work out and lead to results. I think I undersold what I was going through with the antibiotic reaction to the doctor, so she might not have been inclined to notice it's the extreme reaction that you get when you have Lyme disease. I did that for eight or nine weeks and things actually improved after that.

I felt mostly normal. Which, to me, was a relief.

The leg stuff never went away, but everything else was pretty much gone. I was fine for about three months, and then the headaches started to come back again. I started to work out that the headaches were related to food, so I went and saw a dietician. They helped me test as much as they could, and we tried a mast cell elimination diet since they still thought I might have Mast Cell Activation Syndrome (MCAS).

We worked out that I was reacting to food or certain

chemicals, but I didn't have any infections or anything else at the time. But this didn't really go away (the Mast Cell). I was still seeing the dietician. She was amazing, and was as helpful as she could be. But I was also aware that there was still something more going on.

I'd stopped seeing the other doctor because I felt like she wasn't getting it, but like I said now I feel like it was partially my fault for not explaining the full severity of things and letting her know just how bad it really was. So I found this other practice in Sydney, where I started working with a naturopath. I chose the practice because there's a doctor there that specializes in integrative health and Lyme, as well. The naturopath did some tests and looked at things, but again wasn't getting anywhere.

Things weren't getting worse, but they still weren't getting better.

She referred me to one of the doctors there who has an integrative approach, who was looking for viruses and bacteria and all those things. She was also able to recognize that something was very wrong, but she wasn't used to seeing patients like me so she passed me onto another doctor at that same clinic. That's the doctor I'm still seeing now, and I have been since early 2020.

They specifically did Lyme testing, finally, and diagnosed me with Lyme disease, although it was a bit tentative. The thoroughness and the approach of the doctors was really comforting and reassuring, and it was good to get a diagnosis, but I'd had a few different ones already so I wasn't really convinced at first.

How many doctors did you see before reaching your official diagnosis?

From the onset of symptoms when I was 27 (in 2017), I saw a total of 12 doctors, who all said the same thing. They saw the immune effects and symptoms but kept saying they couldn't pinpoint what was going on.

What was the treatment journey like?

There weren't a whole lot of early treatments because most of the doctors I saw early on weren't able to figure out what was even going on. It was like they would do their tests for what they thought I had, and when it wasn't that, they'd pass me onto the next one. As I mentioned, I did take some antibiotics during the journey to getting diagnosed, since they assumed that bacterial or viral infections may be at play.

Most of the antibiotics made me very ill and in some instances, I couldn't even finish the dose or round of treatment that was prescribed. Of course I thought this was weird, especially with one antibiotic that was specifically designed to be "easier" to handle. But since I minimized things to the doctor, it was never made apparent that it was related to the Lyme (which we also still didn't know about at that point).

Once I was diagnosed in 2020, we started going down the Lyme treatment path to determine whether we could address or improve any of the symptoms I was dealing with. I can't speak to the specifics of the treatment or the doctors I'm seeing, for privacy reasons, but suffice it to say it's fairly standard protocol for Lyme patients.

We did do a few trial treatments to make sure that I wasn't

going to have a reaction, or that if I did, it was exactly what Lyme patients would have. Then, over a period of months, I kept getting the treatment, managing side effects, and trying to see if I was going to get results.

I was fortunate to have a doctor who was very engaged, always available, and very interested in how you were feeling. They were very responsive and made sure it suited me, first and foremost.

In 2021, I started to get fatigue and we thought it was related to the treatment or my other health issues. It came and went, and it wasn't anything major, so it just kind of got written off. The treatment was working well otherwise and I was doing mostly better. Most importantly, there weren't really any new symptoms. Eventually, we started to wean off the treatments just to see if I was better.

This was in 2022, and I actually had about two months where I was doing great with no treatments or anything. Then, the fatigue came back for about a month. At this point, I was really active, which I regret in retrospect. Given what I was going through, I was pushing it far too hard. I would go to the gym twice a week and run two or three times a week.

We went back on support supplements and medications in case the fatigue was related to a resurgence of Lyme. The fatigue got better and at this point, I kind of considered myself to be in remission because everything else was going well. I think the fatigue had been building and eventually just spilled out and got really bad during mid-2022. I got a sore throat that I just wrote off as a throat infection, but when it didn't go away, I decided to see a doctor.

I think it stressed me more because you go back into that "sick" mentality and it wears on your body. The chronic fatigue issues are annoying because I'm an over-doer. I've got a busy job and a life that's active, so I have to be careful not to push myself too much. In a perfect world, I think I would have come out of the Lyme treatment and taken some time off work or find a less stressful job that can give my body time to relax. I think having a busy job is hard when your body needs to stop.

I started a neuroplastic program, called the Gupta program. It's basically focused on retraining the brain. When you have a "sick" mentality, you have to retrain your brain away from the worry and the sickness at the unconscious level so that you can be the active, healthy person that you are after Lyme.

And that leads us up to today, basically.

What does your worst day look like?

On the worst days, my body is painful. You become a prisoner to your body and the physical symptoms of chronic fatigue. Then, there's the mental side of things where you get discouraged and depressed when you have to give up the things you love. I can't go to the gym as much or run as much as I'd like, so when that's taken away, you get frustrated. Sometimes I push too hard, and sometimes the fatigue is so bad that I can't even fathom moving at all.

How has Lyme impacted your life?

As I said, up until I was 27, I was very active, very fit, and ate fairly well. I had always done really well at work, and everything was fine. Then, I kind of had this hard stop because you don't know what's happening and you don't have control and you're at the mercy of the medical system where you're usually just a number.

It's changed my life completely at a very fundamental level. I think that I'm one of the lucky ones because I've been able to be motivated and push through and persist to get answers from the doctors and make them keep looking for answers. But it's absolutely changed every aspect of my life. It's made my life more restricted. My choices are limited regarding where I can live because of the need for Lyme-literate doctors.

I can't move home because it's not recognized in New Zealand. I just feel very constrained in all my choices and the things that I do. I had to adjust my fashion sense and find a way to live without wearing trousers since I still have the leg issue. I can probably wear trousers like two days a week. Fortunately, my work is very casual, and I can wear shorts without incident.

Has your family been supportive through your Lyme journey?

I think it's been precarious because I'm here and they're in New Zealand, so they only know what I tell them. I think when you see someone and they're sick, it's more believable, in a way, especially with something like Lyme. It was particularly hard in the first two years when even I didn't really understand what was going on. I was trying to explain to my family that I'm going to all these doctor's appointments and that I need financial support because it's not covered by insurance or anything, and so forth.

My relationship with them now is great. I think at the beginning, it was difficult to explain because I didn't even

have answers and felt a little like it doesn't make sense
and is hard to follow because of all the back and forth
and maybes. My mom works in the health professions so
she kind of has an idea of the medical side of things, but
that can be bad, too, because she'll go into "nurse mode"
instead of "mom mode" sometimes.

My dad is very "Kiwi"—he's reserved, thoughtful, easygoing.
He's very "Dad." He doesn't get the medical stuff, so I felt
at the beginning like I had to validate myself but I think
that was more putting pressure on myself than them doing
anything, of course. He kind of just asks how my health is
going and leaves it at that, and I know what he means and
that he means well.

Have you had any friends or other support along the way?

I've got a great group of friends here in Sydney. I had a
partner, Sam from 2018 to 2020, and he still helps me
with so much stuff because he's close, even though we've
broken up. I definitely feel like I have plenty of support.
At first, I kind of suffered in silence and kept to myself
because I didn't want to bother anyone, you know. I'm not
like that anymore, though. I do still push myself and try to
be independent, but I know I have a great support network
and I use them when I need them.

Is there anything in your personal care routine that really helps you?

I think that being outdoors and being active (or as active
as you can be), is one of the best things that you can do.
Especially for Lyme treatment, when you have so much
stuff running through your bloodstream, I feel like it's
really important to keep your body moving even if it's a

little at a time.

At the moment, with the fatigue side of things, I've been doing more audiobooks. I used to read a lot before, but now I don't always have the mental capacity to absorb the information and process things. It's been great, because I'm reading a lot of things I probably wouldn't have otherwise, giving me back the joy of reading and the ability to share with others and interact, and so forth.

I do use infrared saunas. They're everywhere, so aside from the obvious cost, I think they're a good way for your internal systems to get moving. It's also got a meditative aspect when you're in the sauna room on your own. It's helped both the Lyme and fatigue.

I think curcumin has been helpful, it's an anti-inflammatory supplement that I take.

How did having Lyme, an "invisible" illness, impact you emotionally?

It's been frustrating, for sure. Early on, I felt a lot of—I think you'd consider it shame, I guess, but like, I didn't want people to know I was sick because no one even knew what was going on. I felt like a burden or like I was troubling people, but that improved over time and I'm not like that now.

I actually saw a therapist for about a year, it was sometime during 2018 when I started that. It was one of the best things I did because it taught me how to change how I think about my condition, my relationships, and the world around me in general. So even though I was frustrated and often felt isolated, I learned that I had to take a different approach and I think, to this day, that's one of the best things that I've done.

Lyme has definitely had an impact on my emotional and mental health, but between therapy and my own perseverance, it was never anything that was too much to handle.

When you think about the future of Lyme patients, are you hopeful there is a cure?

Yes, totally. I am hopeful, but I think a lot needs to happen. The unfortunate thing is that more than testing and new medications, we need the medical profession to understand and accept that Lyme exists and that it is a serious and chronic condition. I think the medical community is getting in the way because they're more concerned about processes than individual patient care.

It takes a lot of time and advocacy to get all that through. But yes, I am hopeful that someday there will be better education, acceptance, and a cure.

Any words of advice, encouragement, etc. that you'd like to offer the rest of the Lyme community?

Just keep going. Trust yourself. Be kind to yourself. And particularly for those who are over-doers, listen to your body. Communicate with people and share what you're going through because that network is what will help you get through. I think just, perseverance—keep pushing through.

"It is during our
darkest moments
that we must focus
to see the light"

- Aristotle

ERICA CARROLL

Pemberton, British Columbia, Canada

Inquisitive

Playful

Dedicated

Erica is still very much in the thick of it, in many ways. She lives in Pemberton, British Columbia, which is about two hours north of Vancouver. She struggles a lot with fatigue and brain fog, which are major issues for many Lyme sufferers. Her story is unique because she was bitten a few times and asked for Lyme tests, unlike many who just get sick and never have a clue until it's too late.

What are three words that describe you?

I actually had to ask some friends on this one. Inquisitive, playful, and dedicated.

Do you have a song that inspired you through this journey?

One song that makes me feel really happy is "One Day" by Matisyahu. He does the song with a whole arena full of people singing it, it's really beautiful and fun.

Where did your journey begin?

When I was 15 or 16, I went for a hike on Vancouver Island with my dogs. It was a rainy day, so I had layers on. When I got home, I took off my coat and sweatshirt, and then I looked in the mirror. Immediately I reacted—there was an engorged tick on my tricep. I just put my sweatshirt over it, pulled it out, and threw it in the toilet. I told my mom and dad, they didn't seem alarmed.

After that first tick bite, I had this sensation of being dissociated. I just felt like there was always this gauze, which I now recognize was brain fog. I also got really bad sore throats and my vitamin levels just dropped. My doctor checked my vitamins at one point and she was like, "Wow, this is crazy how depleted you are." Hypoglycemia and anxiety also started around that time, even though I didn't know what that was at the time.

I would get really overwhelmed very easily, I struggled with sensory overload and social situations, and couldn't figure out where it came from or how to stop it. My shoulder started acting up, too. My range of motion was off, my neck was tight and crunchy, and there was just pain and stiffness that was often unbearable.

When I was about 20, I was hiking in the mountains again, and when I came home, I had two black ticks on me. I remember being in the back of the car and freaking out. We went into the house and my friend's boyfriend pulled them out with tweezers and that was the end of it.

However, I asked my doctors for 20 years to test me. Every time, I was like, "I was bitten by these ticks, should we test for Lyme or anything?" In grade eight, we had a class where we studied Lyme disease and Rocky Mountain Spotted Fever, specifically. It was rather unusual, but I never forgot it. That probably helped me to a certain degree, but I still couldn't get doctors to listen.

They were always dismissive.

"Oh no, let's check your iron."

"Oh, you're depressed."

"Oh, you're not sleeping, here are sleeping pills."

I never really thought about it—I was like, okay, yeah, you're probably right. The world I used to live in didn't prioritize health. For me, it wasn't until I got the diagnosis that everything connected. That started with the domino effect of all the body systems collapsing one by one. Then, I started working professionally as an actor and it was really hard. It wasn't until I was about 35 that I was in so much physical pain on a regular basis that I said to my friends, "I think I might have what they call 'chronic pain.' I don't think this is normal."

For a long time, I honestly thought people just lived in this kind of pain and I was weak or incapable, or what have you. My mom and sister also work in healthcare, so it was one of those situations where you trust the medical system because they're supposed to be the ones who know what they're talking about.

I feel like my voice has been affected, I struggled with nausea cycles, chemical sensitivities, and so many other things. I developed light sensitivity, and then eventually vertigo. And that's what did me in.

Let me digress. When I was in Canada, I was getting massages on my neck weekly. Then, I went to Ireland and thought I'd be fine without them. Of course, that didn't work out. Things just got worse and worse, and then one morning I woke up. I felt like my eyes were moving. I didn't even know what vertigo was or realize that it was the room that was moving at the time. I remember falling down the stairs to my aunt and panicking that something was wrong with my eyes. They sent me to an ear, nose, and throat doctor. The vertigo had subsided by that time, and they said that I had nystagmus, which is where your eye moves uncontrollably, but it wasn't; it was vertigo.

Then, I realized there was black mold on the window in the bedroom that I was sleeping in. I didn't know that I had any issues with mold, but also didn't know that I had Lyme. So, vertigo came and went seasonally. I went to ENTs here, and they were like, "You have to just push through, and it will sort itself out."

I was also studying yoga teacher training at the time, and I'd fall over mid-pose and the instructor was like, "Oh my gosh, are you okay?"

"Yeah, it's fine. I just have really bad vertigo."

Maybe I shouldn't have been trying to do yoga, but I am so tough because of what I've been through. I have functioned so much because I had to, I suppose.

What was your journey to a diagnosis like?

I am fortunate now to have a great doctor that I get along really well with. We have a great relationship and she's really worked to advocate for Lyme, both with me and with other patients. That wasn't always the case, of course. I've sat in plenty of rooms with plenty of doctors who completely negate the notion of Lyme disease.

When I got my Lyme diagnosis, I was referred to what's called the Critical Chronic Disease Program at BC Women's Hospital, which was formerly called the Lyme Disease Program, but it got "rebranded." This was a year-long program that they put you in where you see a physiotherapist, therapist, pain management professionals, and so forth.

Essentially, it's designed to help you get a variety of treatments and options that may help you cope with what you're dealing with in your chronic disease. I actually got a letter from the British Columbia CDC saying something to the effect of, "We will treat your patient as long as she agrees to acknowledge that her Lyme diagnosis could be the result of a false positive test."

It was very curt, and was written in such a way that it seemed off, even to my doctor. When I had my intake for the program, the nurse saw me first and took the information. After that, the doctor came in and reviewed the information, then looked at me and went, "Oh, so you think you were bitten by a tick?"

"No, I was bitten."

"Oh, okay. And where did this take place?"

"On Vancouver Island."

"Oh, okay. So you think—"

And he kept on like that, wording it like that as if to dissuade me. I got tested through Armin Labs in Germany and another place in New Jersey. Armin Labs showed borrelia miyamotoi and bartonella.

He said, "So you acknowledge that this is most likely a false positive?"

I said, "How many tests would you like for you to conclude a 'positive' positive? Because I can do that for you." He didn't really care for that response, but after a moment we just carried on.

So, I completed the program and what I deduced from this year-long experience was that I had to just come to terms with the fact that I have something called an 'energy envelope' and that I only have so much in that envelope. I have to live my life with what I have there, and that's that. I don't think it was an entire waste of time. I met a lot of great people there. Plus, information that I had learned I could compare to the medical system and so forth.

On the very last day when they were wrapping up, there were two nurses. I said, "Okay, you're done?"

"Yep."

I said, "So, we're not going to discuss parasites, mold, metals, EMF exposure? We're not going to discuss Lyme, vector-borne illnesses, anything?"

They just sat there and blinked, and then wrote a note which probably went in my file.

I was appalled. We're just supposed to live with this and there's nothing else that you can do. What about, say, sinus infections? What about root canals? What about all of these things that contribute to systemic issues? And of course, they didn't have the answers. So once I realized I wasn't going to get help there, I realized I'd have to take the bull by the horns.

One day, I was working on this show called Supernatural. I was standing there with this blade, playing an angel. We did a take, and the sound guy came over and was like, "I've just got to move your microphone. We can hear your heart."

Just on that day, standing up was really hard, I was so lightheaded, and my heart was working really hard just so I could stand there and do my role.

I've been working all these years and I'm having this certain set of symptoms, and it was all the same, until I went to Russia. There are certain medical things you have to do before you go to Russia—vaccines, so forth. So I got a couple of vaccinations and flew to Russia and started working. Every single day started getting worse. I barely functioned. I would sleep, do my work, and come back home and sleep more. Everything got exponentially worse.

Then, when I got home, I told my doctor that I got a shot before I left and thought I needed a booster. She knew what I was talking about and gave me the booster, and then I started getting pain in my face, my teeth, my eyes, even my tongue. I went back in April, and she told me I actually needed a different booster, she gave it to me, no big deal.

Except that it was a big deal. I found out that I had what was known as trigeminal neuralgia, essentially the nerve and the vein were touching and it's known as one of the most painful conditions a person can have. When I got that last booster, I was supposed to go to an audition afterward. It was totally in my wheelhouse, it was easy, I was ready. And then, I remember, I was doing the scene and my brain just went blank.

So I stopped, took a minute, and started again.

Then, my brain blanked a second time.

And a third time.

Finally, the casting director suggested that I go outside and get a little air and then come back and try again. At the same time, the pain is escalating so severely that I can't even work anymore. At one point, I literally collapsed on the floor because of the pain. So, I can't state facts or say anything for anyone else, but I can tell you that every single time I got one of those injections, I got exponentially worse.

The doctors told me I would need surgery to put a piece of Teflon between the nerve and the vein.

I was like, "Um, no."

I was put on oxycodone and Tegretol to help with nerve pain. It took away all my creativity and the side effects were dreadful. I was sent to a neurologist who said that this was just what I was going to have to stay on, and that I might need a liver or kidney transplant in four or five years. That was the last time I went to a normal doctor about this.

I finally got my GP to test me, but it came back negative, to which I thought, "Oh okay, I don't have Lyme," because I didn't know how ineffective the testing was.

Then, about half a year later, a friend came over and told me that a friend of hers had just gotten diagnosed with Lyme disease. I asked where, and of course it was through a naturopath. So I went to the same naturopath and named off all my symptoms and told my story. We did the testing and it came back positive.

How did you feel when you were first diagnosed?

I was honestly relieved and kind of excited, at first. I actually went into my agency and was all excited telling them, "Hey guys, I have Lyme!"

And of course, they were questioning why this was a good thing. And to me, it was like, well now I know the problem so I can just go and get better. That's how I felt at first. Then, I started down the rabbit hole and became instantly overwhelmed.

I work with Dietrich Klinghardt. Why did I find this person? It's interesting. It was about three or four years prior that my dog got sick. She got cancer in her lungs. I had gone through testing everything in my house that I could. I tested for asbestos, mold, anything I could think of. Then, I heard something about EMFs. I didn't really know anything about it, but I had someone come in and test everything. I noticed that my dog was sleeping next to the router, and the level of radiation coming off the router was staggering.

I immediately stopped using WiFi after that and watched a show called Take Back Your Power. In that show was Dr. Dietrich Klinghardt, talking about EMFs and other things that can cause issues. I kind of made a mental note and left it at that.

What was the treatment journey like?

Once I got my diagnosis of Lyme disease, I started antibiotics and some other treatments with the naturopath that had done the testing for me. Then, I just got this intuition that I needed to stop. Something inside of me was saying, "Don't do this. This isn't going to help you."

It's not that I have an aversion to allopathic medicine. For me, I just had this feeling that the antibiotics weren't right for me. I knew that I needed to go farther because I knew that this was a longer infection. Which led me to Dr. Klinghardt.

When I got my Lyme diagnosis, I remembered seeing him in the documentary. I looked him up and it turned out that he had a clinic in Washington state. That's only a three-hour drive from Vancouver. I remember when I first walked into the clinic, the Sophia Health Institute. I walked in and they didn't roll their eyes.

I just remember the relief I felt. I finally felt like someone understood after years of feeling like I was just a hypochondriac. That was probably more important than any treatment I could have found.

How has Lyme impacted your life?

Well, for one, it caused me to give up my career, which I

worked really hard for and loved. It's been seven or eight years now that I haven't been able to work. I crash, then I get up, and I usually have about two hours of a day where I can function well. Trying to function like other people is not possible at this point.

There are some days when I wish someone would just take over for a little while. There are different parts of me. There is the very basic human energy, then there is my spiritual side. There's the positive person and the realist.

There's one side of me that's like, wow, what a gift. This woke me up and made me see a system that's so corrupt and messed up and that I no longer subscribe to it. How grateful I am to know that healing is within me. I'm so grateful for the things I've learned.

Then I've got the other side where I wake up where I feel like I'm going to vomit, my skin hurts, I can't look at the light, my eyes feel like they're popping out, I've got nerve pain, my back is flaring—and I am just in a ball sobbing and want to give up on everything.

Do you feel like there's anything that you've missed out on?

My career, which was going really well and I had worked so hard for. I felt ripped off for all that effort. But I've got that balance that I know that none of it was a waste. It was all an accomplishment, a learning experience, and I met so many great people along the way.

There's also part of me that's like I'm here for a specific journey. This is my journey, this is what I came here for, so now it's time to figure out how to do it. Wow, I'm tough. I am really proud of myself and of how far I've come. I know good things are coming. I don't know what level of healing I'll reach, but I know that good and bad will come and go. The surrender has helped a lot.

What treatments and things did you do that were most helpful?

The TN therapy was helpful. I also had a root canal that cleared up some of my root canal and teeth issues. I had a splint to relax my jaw because I was clenching too much. A lot of that also subsided when I turned off my WiFi, though.

Before I went to the Sophia Institute, they wanted to make sure that you weren't living in a moldy environment because if so, the treatment wouldn't be effective. So I had my house tested for mold and you couldn't see any, but it was definitely there. Getting rid of the mold and making sure I avoid it now is still big.

Once I started going to Sophia, using homeopathics and herbals was really effective for me. I do supplements, teas, all of it. Very rarely we would use disulfiram, but I couldn't tolerate it. I got neuropathy so I didn't use it for very long.

Emotional therapy also helped, including work on things like boundaries and learning to know when my body was saying "yes" and "no." I also did well with detoxing, and I think that's essential for an ongoing relief. I do a lot of meditation, tapping, foot baths, and I use red light.

I have a frequency device that I got from someone who actually lived close to me. I started using this and I started getting a HERCs reaction, but I used it for shorter periods and worked my way up until I could wear it for as long as eight hours at a time.

**When you think about the future of Lyme patients, are
you hopeful there is a cure?**

Not unless the system is changed. Again, there are theories
around the origin and elaborate nature of this disease. I
feel like there's a cure for everything. I just don't know what
it will be. The cure is different for everyone, though, right?
For some people it may be physical, while for others it may
be emotional or spiritual.

I look at Lyme as a complex, not a single bacterium. I don't
think a vaccine is going to get rid of Lyme disease. There's
the thing that's contributing to the symptom fallout, and
then there's the fallout. There's the healing from these
symptoms, even if you don't have Lyme actively, and I think
too often people are left to figure it out for themselves.

But yes, I will say yes, I am hopeful that there will be some
form of a cure in the future.

**Any words of advice, encouragement, etc. that you'd like
to offer the rest of the Lyme community?**

Write down every single symptom and element in your
body because it's going to change and it's so gradual
that you may not notice. There's so many times where I
don't realize how much progress I've made, and that's so
disheartening.

This is an onion. You have so many layers that you're going
to have to deal with. You're definitely not the same person
going in as you are coming out.

I think it's important to learn to be still and reconnect with
that inner voice. I think we live in a society where we have
been dumbed down so much that we don't even hear that

voice anymore, but when you're diagnosed with Lyme, you have to.

You have to learn and listen as much as you can.

You have to get someone that you trust to help you advocate for yourself.

And find your coping mechanisms.

You are the expert on you—don't waver under the doctors' authority.

Finally, I hope this will help you find the courage to speak up.

ZUZANA MARTAN

Prague, Czech Republic

Honest

Direct

Faithful

Before we even began the interview, Zuzana immediately jumped in to set the stage for her story:

I just wanted to say that for me, the experience is completely shocking and unacceptable at a human level, to be honest… this is something I believe is just not right at all. I really struggle with it because it doesn't make any sense. I used to trust the doctors, but I cannot after this experience. It turns your world completely upside down, and I'm still digesting what's happening, actually.

Zuzana lives in the Czech Republic and is one of the few people I've encountered that didn't get Lyme from a tick. She says that when she was bitten, it was by a black fly, not a tick. Let's hear the story in her own words.

What are three words that describe you?

Honest, direct, and I would say, faithful. I still have faith, despite all that has happened.

Where did your journey begin?

I remember it because it was on my left shoulder that I got bitten. It was an aggressive bite. I felt a pain and intuitively slapped the shoulder. Apparently, one of the doctors who were more up to date was saying that it was a shame we weren't in contact when I got bit because he knew that flies could also cause this.

It happened in June 2022 and then in August, I started getting brain fog that was just awful. Once, I went out and I didn't know how to return. Thankfully, two hours later it disappeared, so I was okay. However, it was still scary. You don't know if you can rely on yourself anymore.

What was your journey to a diagnosis like?

I didn't really have a "journey," so to speak. I was told by a doctor that I probably had Lyme, when I saw one that knew about it, and then I was tested and diagnosed. It is harder with doctors here after the fact, because they only have about five minutes per patient and I'm trying to be informed and ask questions and know what is going on, but they just want to rush through and get the quickest answer and go onto the next one.

What was the treatment journey like?

I think I had 200 milligrams of doxycycline for 14 weeks and then I was told I was cured. I was not cured, and in fact, I had never been so sick in my life. The test that you can do in the Czech Republic is the Western blot test, where I can see four types of Lyme that are being tested and I have antibodies for all four of them. Thanks to herbs, however, I am much better today. I am not cured, but I am stable.

How did you find your way to feeling better?

I found an herbalist on a Facebook group that was recommended to me. I made an appointment and am now a regular patient. They are holistic and look at all the different things. I had started to do that myself, but here I was able to get support, not only in terms of herbal treatments, but in supporting me and discussing my situation and informing me of what's going on.

They created mixes that were uniquely designed for me and my issues, of which I'm currently taking four. They are for specific issues I had, and include a host of supplements. I also had to completely change my diet. I kept losing weight and was having lactose issues. I am currently lactose-free and gluten-free. I also invested in an infrared sauna, which I couldn't live without. The infrared treatments really make a huge difference. I also take walks and do meditation. That's basically my must-do list to feel somewhat normal.

How has Lyme impacted your life?

When the season comes, I start to get very afraid of all the flying insects. I can't help it; it's a subconscious fear. I remember the original bite being so painful, and knowing what it led to, it makes me want to stay indoors. I am trying to deal with it because I have to, but I can't tell you how difficult it is now, after everything that I've been through.

That fear of being reinfected and not really knowing what's going on with your body, it's really, really hard. I cannot trust the doctors anymore. I used to, but after this, I just can't anymore. I was being treated aggressively, ignored by doctors, and gaslighted. It's still hard to comprehend.

It was also really soul crushing, because from someone who was very active and busy and always doing things, I was now barely able to take care of myself. Unfortunately, for a long period of time, nobody would believe me. Now, my closest family, my husband, and others see that I'm getting better, they believe me.

What was your lowest point?

It was two months after I got infected in August, because that was when the mental issues started. I was weak, physically I was in pain, my brain wasn't working right, the doctors were dismissing me, my family and husband were dismissing me. I couldn't even think about my own health and getting help because my mental capacity was pretty much switched off entirely.

It was so horrible. It was completely blank.

Another day I woke up and I couldn't feel anything. I was completely blank on the ability to feel. I also had these crazy heartbeats, so it was very stressful. I also started having trouble breathing, which added to it. I think the worst was feeling frightened, lost, and hopeless.

Then, there was one time when I was at the hospital and my husband was with me, and apparently the doctor was convincing enough that by the time we left, it was almost like my husband was against me again. He was talking like the doctor was about psychiatry and maybe I was fine and so forth, and it felt really, really lonely and terrifying to have the closest person to you not on your side.

Do you feel like you've missed out on anything because of Lyme?

I am still missing out. I am still missing a normal life. I was always really active, really great at my job, social, and able to juggle many things. I was the type of person who liked to multitask. I can't do that anymore and I feel like I've lost an important part of myself because of that. It's still me, but it's me with restrictions, and that's really hard. For example, this weekend it was my mom's and husband's birthdays and I was not well enough to go to Brunel to celebrate with them.

When you don't have Lyme, you have freedom. Now, you don't have a choice. You feel like if you don't do all the right things, it will impact how you feel. It really affects your freedom. I'm not traveling, either. I haven't been anywhere for the past two years. When I go to Brunel to visit my parents, it's like a project.

It changes my life completely. I wouldn't risk going to any gatherings right now because I don't want to risk getting sick. I got a good remote job in November. It's not in my field of finance because of my restrictions, but it is a good job and I am lucky that it's flexible. When I said I needed part-time, remote work in my field of finance, I couldn't find anything.

I've always been open and honest, now I'm isolated and feel like I can't talk to anyone because I'm being forced to lie about my Lyme. And I refuse to lie. So I was left isolated a lot of the time and left behind by friends.

What is the response from your family and friends now?

As I said, no one really believed me at first. It was so difficult. Even at certain points, my mother would say, "Oh I believe you, but I don't know how to help you." Eventually, they all became supportive, as I said. I can now talk about my Lyme openly and they believe me because they've seen the proof of it getting better. However, it's still difficult to talk about the details. I am grateful that I have my herbalist because I can talk to them about everything.

My husband also started showing symptoms, and he got tested. He was showing antibodies, but regular doctors kept saying he was not infected. He's being treated by my herbalist, as well, and he's better now, too. So, he went from really not believing me at first to understanding it firsthand. Neither of us are cured, but things are much better, and he is even less severe than I am in terms of symptoms.

Have you found any friends or support along the way?

I joined a lot of different groups online, but at first it was scary. I did find a Facebook group for Lyme in the UK, and they really saved my life. If it weren't for them, I would not be here today. The mentorship program from Global Lyme Alliance was great, too. I was able to connect with someone for an hour a day, multiple times a week, to have someone to talk to about Lyme and feel less isolated.

Is there anything that you do at home to bring you joy between all of the treatments?

I think a lot of what helps me is going out into nature. Obviously, I still have some fear, but I absolutely need to get out. Long walks, even if I was tired, were always on my list of things to do. Another thing I love is the infrared sauna. It's really, really helpful. It's one of my favorite parts of the day, in fact.

What is really helping me now is that I'm able to work. I can't do what I used to, but I can work and support myself and contribute. I was able to find a role that utilized my financial knowledge and am now back in touch with people. We have face-to-face time on calls and it's nice to feel like I'm slowly crawling back to life.

When you think about the future of Lyme patients, are you hopeful there is a cure?

Yes, I am hopeful that someday there is a better future for Lyme patients and I really believe that if we talk about it, it can be resolved.

I have a DREAM...

That one day we will all live in a world FREE of Lyme Disease

KENZIE VATH

Orange County, California

Driven

Compassionate

Authentic

My story starts off with a young girl from Southern California, a place that knows little to nothing of Lyme disease or the ticks that cause it. The timing of the onset of symptoms impacted my education greatly. I was immediatly labeled with learning disabilities, such as; dyslexia. Classifying me with the idea of having less intelligence than the average person.

I didn't know it then, but clearly that was not the problem. I'm actually quite intelligent. But the neurological Lyme symptoms had taken hold and I began disconnecting from my developmental milestones. Feeling less like myself, even before I was really old enough to understand what that meant. In order to align with the style of the book, I had myself interviewed.

For those of you who are still wondering who I am and why I've written this book, let's dive in.

What are three words that describe you?

I love this question, but three words are not enough to describe me. Mostly driven, I notice this is a common thread between us Lyme warriors. I would also say I am compassionate, authentic and just to be extra colorful.

Do you have a song that inspired you through this journey?

Tired (Kygo Remix) by Alan Walker. Anything Kygo inspires me.

Where did your journey begin?

My Lyme journey began right about the same time I was learning to read and write. No one realized it at the time, but looking back, it's clear that what I was going through what was neurological Lyme.

Letters, words, and numbers did not come easy to me. I struggled with memory and to form proper sentences or relate my feelings to the appropriate words. I was often frustrated because I was constantly being corrected by my family, teachers, and other adults in my life. I continued to fall behind and was not able to keep up with my class-mates, no matter how hard I tried or how badly I wanted to.

Dyslexia, special education, "not very bright" … these were just a few of the things I'd overheard regarding my incapabilities.

Some things just were not adding up. I was unable to express the disconnect in my brain. My thoughts made me feel as if I was in a straitjacket, screaming in my head and no one could hear me. I realized I had lost myself.

As I got older, I learned how to cope and ignore my disabil-ities or use them to my advantage. I did not want anyone to know how bad I struggled. I became very self-conscious in school. Reading aloud, handwriting in class, and daily spelling quizzes became daunting tasks, leading to debilitating anxiety. It was so unnatural for me to be shy, introverted, and anxious. I often missed school due to the symptoms that progressively got worse. Anxiety became the loudest voice, leading to excruciating stomach pains that kept me home. I felt captive and started to miss out, avoiding people, saying no to friends, and not attending social gatherings.

As I got older, the issues progressively got worse. Brain fog kicked in—this feeling of trying to think with a thick cloud. Other days my head felt like concrete and I could barely hold it up in class. The brain fog was so frustrating. I saw many specialists and would find myself in the appointments saying, "that's right, thank you mom," since I couldn't even remember what my symptoms were. One morning, I woke up and my joints were stiff, they had no mobility. As if my body had been in a cast for years and I was learning how to move, how to walk, for the first time.

Then came the fatigue. This was not the typical, "I'm tired and just had a bad night's sleep." This was a very heavy feeling throughout my entire body. I was paralyzed, almost cemented to my bed. It took every ounce of energy just to sit up, get my feet on the floor, push with my legs to stand, and then pause there for a minute because in many cases I would get dizzy and almost faint upon standing.

I would take a few steps to the bathroom, immediately placing my hands on the counter because I couldn't even hold myself up to look in the mirror. My face was pale and dull, eyes sunken and half-masted, my hair was thin and drab... I was frail, withering away and felt like I was slowly dying. Movement no longer felt natural, and every ounce of daily exertion would put me in bed for a week, if not two.

Physical pain would fluctuate. It was moderate through-out high school, but some days were more severe than others. The weather would play a role, exacerbating my symptoms,. Damper days were more of a challenge. Looking back, I think this was partially due to mold toxicity. By the end of the day, I felt like I hiked 15 miles, got hit by a Mack truck, and was drugged with a tranquilizer. I was basically unresponsive to my friends and family let alone emotional. I would just curl up in bed and shut out the world.

What was your journey to a diagnosis like?

My mother did all she could, taking me to any specialist

she could find in the hopes of finding an answer. Her once healthy, outgoing, energetic, and lovely daughter became a moody, angry, depressed, negative, and introverted stranger. She knew something was wrong, but couldn't find a reason. So she started making appointments and when one didn't work out, we'd go to another. I remember going from one doctor to the next, reciting my story over and over, trying to remember every single detail in order.

The driving, the questioning, the testing, the supplements—it all became exhausting on top of everyday life. They ran hundreds, if not thousands of tests over the course of this journey. Trying to find an answer was like trying to find a needle in a haystack. Some results would indicate low iron, inflammatory markers, candida, and more. but nothing would actually explain the breadth of the symptoms I was experiencing.

And of course, many physicians were even skeptical that I had anything wrong with me in the first place. General anxiety and depression were the first obvious diagnoses. What they did not know at the time is that these were symptoms, not the root cause. The joint pain was written off as growing pains. My behavior changes were attributed to being a "dramatic teenager" and the most common response we heard was:

"It's all in her head. She should see a psychiatrist and get on medication."

I was gaslighted and ignored by the professionals, the people who were supposed to be helping me. Appointments ended in tears, psychiatric prescriptions (that rarely worked), supplements, and endless bills that were not covered by insurance. From the onset of my symptoms to the year I received my diagnosis, I spent a decade suffering in silence, fighting a medical system that had no idea just how real and serious chronic Lyme disease could be.

I attended a talk by Dr. Dino, who was promoting Envita Clinic at the time. He was speaking about their amazing results with terminal cancer treatment, and something called Lyme disease.

The presentation about Lyme brought crawling chills through my body, a rush of heat to my head, and tears to my eyes. My heart pounding with adrenaline and my insides welling with hope, I looked at my mom and she knew, too, that we may finally have an answer for all of these years of suffering.

We immediately spoke to Dr. Dino after his presentation, and he suggested we come to Arizona for a few days to go through extensive testing. These days were long and tireless. A month later we had a call set with a lead doctor at the clinic. They called and said the words I didn't even know I'd been waiting to hear:

"Kenzie, you are positive for Lyme disease: babesia, bartonella, and rickettsia (Rocky Mountain Fever). Your CD57 is 45 and the fact that you're functioning at the level you are, is a miracle."

I finally received a proper diagnosis and a label for my symptoms. A word for what was wrong with my body and why I no longer was myself. That little girl who for so long felt like suicide was her only option now had an answer. I pulled her out of that dark hole and I felt relieved. But nothing prepared me for the journey ahead to recovery.

How many doctors did you see before reaching your official diagnosis?

Over the course of 10 years, I saw dozens of different general practitioners, along with specialists, herbalists, and everything else you could imagine. I lost count but took a search in my contacts and had 32 numbers saved. In total, it was probably closer to 50.

What was the treatment journey like?

The journey of treatment should almost get its own book. I dropped out of college and moved to Arizona. Packed up a Uhaul my Goldendoodle June and my mom and I made the drive to Scottsdale. Found an apartment near the clinic that would be our home for the next three months. We brought along crafts and games thinking we could spend some quality time together.

I'm sure my mom was thinking, a few months to get back her baby girl after sending me off to college would be fun. Treatment was nothing close to fun. I was hooked up to IVs from 8am to 4pm. Took zofran daily to avoid 24-hour nausea. I would start with oxy bosh, essentially mixing my blood with oxygen and putting it back into the body to help fight the Lyme bacteria. I did multiple IV antibiotics daily, high dose Vitamin C, hydrogen peroxide, ozone, infrared sauna and the supplements could have sunk a ship. I smelled terrible even after taking a shower, my body was seriously detoxing. My mom would bathe me since I barely had the energy to stand and could not get my PICC line wet, which could lead to infection.

If my memory is correct, I think it was about a month in and I started to use a cane to walk. My mom and I would make jokes all the time about being old. It was the only way we could make light of the situation. When we came home from treatment, we would put on Golden Girls or Bonanza since we only had basic cable. I'd fall asleep to those shows and they are still a comfort nostalgic to me today. Treatment made me even more ill, which seemed impossible. The doctors recommended I continue after the initial 3 months but my body and mind couldn't do it anymore and I made the decision to go home. Treatment continued at home as well as a complex lifestyle change.

How has Lyme impacted your life?

I spent a lot of my younger years in a very dark place. I was struggling with all of these things and simultaneously missing out on a "normal" childhood because of what I was going through, which made plenty of room for anxiety and depression to run rampant. For a long time, I had gotten to such a low point that suicide was starting to seem like the only real, feasible option to get relief from all the pain, emotional trauma, and shame I had from this invisible illness.

I wasn't able to participate in a lot of things. I couldn't do things with friends and enjoy the "normal" childhood and teenage years that most kids have. It was hard to grow up sick, and the battle for an accurate diagnosis definitely affected my level of trust in the medical system.

However, Lyme has also impacted my life positively. It turned me into a huge advocate for the Lyme community and has given me the opportunity to serve on the board of GLA, as well as to publish this book. Although it was the biggest, longest, and most difficult struggle of my life. Lyme has given me the opportunity to have a bigger purpose and I believe that's why God put me here.

Has your family been supportive through your Lyme journey?

My mom was my biggest advocate, my voice, and my security blanket. Given the age I was when I was going through all this, she was instrumental in getting the right diagnosis and treatment. Doctors don't listen to kids. They barely listen to adults, in some cases. Fortunately, my mom was willing to talk to every doctor she could until she found one that would listen and help us.

My family was as supportive as they could be. Most of them really didn't understand what I was going through and knew nothing of Lyme disease. A few of my friends stuck around, but many disconnected from me since I never felt well enough to be normal. But my mom is the reason I am alive.

Have you found any friends or support along the way?

I have met many people along my Lyme journey, including many fellow Lyme warriors with amazing stories that are even more involved and lengthy than my own. I have also found connections with friends and those in the medical community, as well as Lyme groups and advocacy organizations like the Global Lyme Alliance. For me, even knowing that there were others out there completely changed things. So naturally, I wanted to get involved and help others.

During the course of writing this book, I've collected another two dozen or so friends, acquaintances, and connections in the Lyme community. And they are all amazingly strong, determined people – it was difficult to narrow down the list of interviews to include because every single one touched me so dearly.

So yes, I have made many great connections and friendships because of my Lyme diagnosis.

What current treatments, routines, and health practices do you have?

Currently I have a full-time job, a mom of three littles and sit on more than a handful of boards among many other things. My life is busy and full but in the best way. Staying busy is part of my health practice, having a purpose and living my life to the fullest really puts things into perspective. I feel as if I missed out on so much and I don't want to miss out anymore. My lifestyle is generally healthy; clean diet, adequate sleep (unless the babies are crying), hydration, basic supplements, meditation or quiet time. I love spending time outside in the sun so anytime I can take a call outside or walk the dogs and kids on the weekends I will.

My body still struggles with general pain and I still struggle a bit with memory. My body will let me know when I make a bad decision like wearing the wrong pair of shoes or eating the cake at a wedding. I try to avoid triggers for me and toxic environments. Today, I'm working on saying no, this is the hardest for me right now. I always take on more and tend to push myself because if I did not struggle with illness I have no idea where I would be. Reflection is also part of my daily health routine. I reflect daily on gratitude and pause to see the joy and happiness in life.

How did having Lyme, an "invisible" illness, impact you emotionally?

As I mentioned, the anxiety and depression that it caused were almost unbearable. I felt "less than" my peers, like I would never fit in, and like I was always going to have to work ten times as hard as everyone else to do the

361

bare minimum. It was, and is, exhausting, mentally and emotionally as much as it is physically. I had a lot of dark days, dark weeks, and even dark years. Eventually, I found my way out, but there was a long time where I wasn't sure I ever would.

Social anxiety made me severely uncomfortable being alone or around new people. I would feel nauseous, my heart would race, and my palms would sweat. This happened at doctors' visits, in school, at home, everywhere. I felt worthless, empty, meaningless, like I was just taking up space and left all alone, with no purpose and no real "life" to be had. For me, the absence of purpose convinced my thoughts there was no reason to live. What should I do next?

My obsession with suicide and how to end my life painlessly cannibalized my thoughts. I wanted the pain and suffering to end. I spent many nights going to bed, asking God to please don't let me wake up.

When you think about the future of Lyme patients, are you hopeful there is a cure?

Absolutely! I know that it's not going to be a "one and done" cure, but I feel that the more we advocate and fight and push for better testing, treatment, answers and education, the closer we will get to finding a solution in the future so that my children and their children don't have to even think about something like chronic Lyme.

How do you feel (or hope) that sharing your story will help?

I've been sharing bits and pieces of my story publicly for a few years now. It was very hard for me to come to a place to be public about my struggles. I never wanted anyone to know. However, I did a talk at women's event and shared a bit of my story with Lyme. I was flooded with people who wanted to ask me more. A mother brought her high school daughter to the event. She has been struggling for quite some time and she pulled her out of school just to come to this event and be inspired by strong women.

She had no idea my story would lead her to answers they have been in search of for years. If my story reaches even one person who is inspired to keep going, keep fighting... that's why I do it. I wanted to share it here because so many people have asked and I want you as the reader to know why this book is personal to me and why I will continue to be an advocate.

My hope is that my story, along with all of the others in this book, will find those who are still struggling. Those who are in dark places. Those who feel "crazy" and are questioning whether the doctors are right about it being all in their head. I want to give them hope and a reason to keep fighting.

Any words of advice, encouragement, etc. that you'd like to offer the rest of the Lyme community?

Don't give up, you can't. I know it seems impossible at times (and sometimes all the time), but don't give up. Also, try your best to not be hard on yourself. Do what you can, be okay with what you can't, and find people to help you and advocate for you when you need it. There is an entire world

For You .

Dear Reader,

You are part of an influential world that can move the needle and make a difference. Share the information you have learned in this book. Educate others about Lyme disease and tick-borne illness. Gift the book to a friend, loved one, or caretaker. Be more aware when enjoying your time in nature; do tick checks. If you feel a need to do more, donate. There are amazing organizations that support patient care and those who are not able to afford treatment. Organizations such as GLA focus on funding promising research in Lyme with the mission to find a cure. Get involved and advocate for what you believe in. Power is in numbers. The more people who get properly diagnosed will force a movement of change. We can be stronger than Lyme. No one deserves to suffer in silence.

The blank pages to follow are for you. Include your story alongside these Lyme Warriors. Add your story to this beautiful collection of Lyme warriors. Be vulnerable and open. Take notes when at your next doctor's appointment so you can make connections to your medical constellation. These pages are open for your words, doodles, pictures and more to release and collect what is in your soul. You are not alone. I am hopeful you will find an answer to your own journey with - or alongside someone with - Lyme disease.

- Kenzie Vath

Share your story .
YOU could save a life .

Your Story

Global Lyme Alliance Community

Join me in breaking the silence and giving hope to all those suffering. Submit your story to be part of the GLA community. We are in this together.

Playlist

Lyme Warrior

A collection of songs curated by Lyme Warriors around the world to inspire and bring hope to those suffering from Lyme and tick-borne illness.

FAQs

To the point

The Ignored Pandemic is here to guide your journey navigating the new or current waters of your diagnosis. The information covered in the previous chapters is meant to be digestible to every reader. The most frequently asked questions are simple and direct responses. They are here to empower you with the current facts. These run the gamut and include everything from basic questions to more specific inquiries, offering something for everyone.

What Is Lyme Disease?

Lyme disease is a condition caused by bacteria that is transmitted by black-legged ticks. It is characterized by a rash around the bite site and symptoms like fever, chills, swollen lymph nodes, headache, fatigue, and muscle or joint pain.

What Is Chronic vs. Acute Lyme?

Chronic Lyme disease refers to those people who have had Lyme for an extended period, either due to it not being properly diagnosed or because treatment was ineffective. It can often lead to other serious health issues and cause lifelong debilitation for many. Acute Lyme disease refers to a condition that is current and active, and that hasn't been left untreated to cause other health issues.

Who Can Get Treated for Lyme Disease?

This is a big question for many people since diagnosis is currently not that effective. Often, more than half of those tested can't be properly diagnosed right away, which can lead to delays in treatment and other concerns. Therefore, if the symptoms are present, Lyme is suspected, and a tick has been involved, many doctors will start antibiotic treatment to be safe. Children can also be treated for Lyme and like adults, the sooner, the better.

What Is the Cure for Lyme Disease?

Currently, there is no single, guaranteed "cure" for Lyme. Many people see a full recovery from the disease with anti-biotic treatment, while others will require complementary therapies and other treatment options for ongoing support. Still more may develop chronic Lyme disease or related symptoms, like arthritis and heart conditions, due to ongoing exposure to the bacteria. Most research is focused on finding better treatments for this reason.

How Can I Prevent Lyme Disease?

There are several ways that you can prepare and protect yourself against the potential for Lyme disease. For starters, you should use tick repellant whenever you're in tick-prone areas outdoors. You should also wear long pants and sleeves, and try to stay out of the tall grasses whenever you can. When you get home, take your clothes off and put them on high heat in the dryer for about 15 minutes. That will ensure that you don't bring any live ticks into the house. Check people and pets for ticks regularly, too, so that they don't have time to do much damage.

What's the Prognosis?

As mentioned, those who are diagnosed and treated early will have the best chances of a full recovery. 10-20% of those who are diagnosed early still develop chronic symptoms, but it is much rarer. If the initial condition is severe or there are existing neurological issues, it becomes much more likely for someone to develop chronic symptoms. For those who are diagnosed later, the prognosis may not be as positive due to chronic symptoms, but improved testing efforts are being researched to help reduce this incidence.

Are People Predisposed to Lyme Disease?

There isn't necessarily a "type" of person that is more likely to get Lyme disease. However, those who are at a higher risk for developing chronic issues, even after antibiotic treatment, include those who have a genetic predisposition or certain immune system variables involved. As mentioned in the research chapter, biomarkers have been identified to help providers diagnose Lyme and determine who is more likely to be affected.

Can You Get Lyme Disease More Than Once?

Yes, you can get Lyme disease multiple times. However many times you get bitten by an infected tick is how many times you can develop this disease. Bear in mind that if you are infected with the same strain time and again, your body will eventually build up some resistance. However, the bacteria in particular can interfere with the memory of your immune system, allowing it to re-attack the body every time you are infected.

This is another area where more research is required. There isn't a lot of data regarding protective immunity or tolerance levels, or insights on reinfection rates for those who have had Lyme in the past.

What Should I Do with the Tick?

In obvious cases of a tick bite, people may have to remove the tick from the skin on their own. It's second nature to throw it out once it's removed, but that isn't the best course of action. You'll want to save the tick and have it available for providers or researchers who want to figure out whether you have been infected. This will also help them learn more about the condition and how to prevent it in the future, as well as identify areas where there may be an increased prevalence of ticks and tick-borne diseases like Lyme.

Can Lyme Disease Affect My Vision?

Lyme disease affects all the neuromuscular activities within the body. Therefore, it can impact a people's vision.

Lyme can create muscle weakness that results in double vision, and it can even exacerbate conditions like peripheral neuropathy. If you are suffering from vision or eye issues, you should visit an eye doctor to get checked out and mention the tick bite if you've had one recently and think Lyme may be a concern.

Do Lyme Vaccines Work?

Although there is promise for the Lyme vaccines that have been developed to date, including their approval by the FDA, it remains to be seen how effective they are. It takes years, and even decades sometimes, to get enough research to make an unbiased opinion on whether something like a vaccine is effective. Currently, these vaccines are showing promise and helping reduce the incidence of Lyme disease in many populations. However, it may not work for everyone.

Can You Die from Lyme Disease?

This is a question that people ask often. It is rare that Lyme disease is immediately a life-threatening condition, but that also depends on who is affected. For example, someone with heart disease or neurological issues is more likely to have serious impact from Lyme disease. This can create complications that eventually lead to serious events like heart attacks or strokes, and eventually end in death. The other important piece of this not often documented is the mental health challenges that come with Lyme. Lyme patients have an increase risk of suicide. Chronic illness is not always something people can live with and some never get the answers, support and help they need. This is a very unfortunate situation and it is critical we bring more awareness around mental health and chronic illness.

There is no shame in asking for HELP.

If you need it PLEASE get it.

Resources

Administrator. (2022, September 23). Eva Sapi ph.d. -
Norsk Lyme borreliose- forening - Norsk Lyme borreliose
- forening - intresseorganisasjon for borrelia-rammede og
pårørende. Norsk Lyme Borreliose- Forening - Norsk Lyme
Borreliose - Forening - intresseorganisasjon for Borrelia-rammede og pårørende - Norsk Lyme Borreliose-Forening
er en landsomfattende intresseorganisasjon for alle som er
blitt langvarig/kronisk syke av Borrelia etter flåttbitt, deres
pårørende, samt andre som er intressert i problematikken/
utviklingen innen området. Retrieved May 2, 2023, from
https://lyme.no/aktuelt/gjesteskribent/eva-sapi-phd/#:~:-
text=It%20has%20been%20proposed%20that,disease%20
protocol%20with%20surprising%20success.

Blakemore, Erin. "Scientists Identify Biomarkers That
Could Help Diagnose Lyme Disease." The Washington
Post, 28 Nov. 2022, www.washingtonpost.com/well-
ness/2022/11/28/lyme-disease-biomarkers-diagnosis/.

CDC. (2020, January 27). Pregnancy and lyme disease -
centers for disease control and prevention. Pregnancy and
Lyme Disease. https://www.cdc.gov/lyme/resources/tool-
kit/factsheets/Pregnancy-and-Lyme-Disease-508.pdf

"Complementary and Alternative Medicine." Lyme Disease
| Complementary and Alternative Medicine | St. Luke's
Hospital, www.stlukes-stl.com/health-content/medi-
cine/33/000102.htm. Accessed 2023.

Cona, Louis A. "Stem Cell Therapy: Lyme Disease Break-
through in 2023?" DVCSTEM, 24 Apr. 2023, www.dvcstem.
com/post/stem-cell-therapy-for-lyme-disease.

Couzin-Frankel, Jennifer. "Long-Underfunded Lyme Disease Research Gets an Injection of Money-and Ideas." Science, 17 Apr. 2019, www.science.org/content/article/long-under-funded-lyme-disease-research-gets-injection-money-and-ideas.

"History of Lyme Disease." Bay Area Lyme Foundation, 9 May 2022, www.bayarealyme.org/about-lyme/histo-ry-lyme-disease/.

Huff, Charlotte. "Unraveling the Mystery of Lyme Disease." American Psychological Association, 1 June 2022, www.apa.org/monitor/2022/06/feature-lyme-disease.
Johns Hopkins Medicine Lyme Disease Research Center, www.hopkinslyme.org/. Accessed 2023.

"Ketamine Infusion for Lyme Disease." Florida Mind Health, www.flmindhealth.com/chronic-lyme-disease-treatment/. Accessed 2023.

"Lyme and Tick-Borne Diseases Research Center." Columbia University Irving Medical Center, 12 Apr. 2018, www.columbia-lyme.org/about-us.

"Lyme Disease Funding | Treatment Guidelines | Symptoms." Lyme Disease Association, 28 Feb. 2023, lymedisea-seassociation.org/.

"Lyme Disease Natural Treatment for Lyme Disease | Hyperbaric Oxygen Therapy." Hyperbaric Medical Solutions, www.hyperbaricmedicalsolutions.com/conditions/non-covered/lyme-disease. Accessed 2023.

"Lyme Disease Research Group." University of New Haven, www.newhaven.edu/research/labs-groups/lyme-disease.php. Accessed 2023.

"Lyme Disease Studies." National Institute of Allergy and Infectious Diseases, www.niaid.nih.gov/clinical-trials/lyme-disease-studies. Accessed 2023.

"Lyme Disease." Centers for Disease Control and Prevention, 19 Jan. 2022, www.cdc.gov/lyme/index.html.
"Lyme Disease." Mayo Clinic, 10 Feb. 2023, www.mayoclinic.org/diseases-conditions/lyme-disease/symptoms-causes/syc-20374651.

Newswire, Ivanhoe. "Stinging Away Lyme Disease with Bee Venom Therapy." WINK News, 29 Apr. 2021, www.winknews.com/2021/04/29/stinging-away-lyme-disease-with-bee-venom-therapy/.

"Our Mission: Eradicate Lyme Disease by 2030." Tufts Lyme Disease Initiative, 2 Jan. 2023, tuftslymedisease.org/.

"The PK Protocol: Chronic Lyme Disease & Chronic Fatigue." Beyond the Bite, 26 June 2015, www.beyondthebite4life.com/2015/06/the-pk-protocol-chronic-lyme-disease-chronic-fatigue.html.

"Rocky Mountain Spotted Fever (RMSF)." Centers for Disease Control and Prevention, 7 May 2019, www.cdc.gov/rmsf/index.html.

Ross, Marty. "Rife Machines for Lyme Disease Treatment." Treat Lyme, www.treatlyme.net/guide/rife-machine-lyme-disease. Accessed 2023
Santarella, Scott. "Be Tick Aware: Tick Bite Prevention Made Easy." Ranger Ready Repellents®, 2023, rangerready.com/blogs/in-the-news/be-tick-aware-tick-bite-prevention-made-easy.

"Signs and Symptoms of Untreated Lyme Disease." Centers for Disease Control and Prevention, 15 Jan. 2021, www.cdc. gov/lyme/signs_symptoms/index.html.
State of Rhode Island: Department of Health, health.ri.gov/ disease/carriers/ticks/. Accessed 2023.

Snowden, J., & Simonsen, K. A. (2022, July 18). Rocky Mountain Spotted Fever (Rickettsia rickettsii). National Library of Medicine. https://www.ncbi.nlm.nih.gov/books/ NBK430881/

"Tick Removal: Medlineplus Medical Encyclopedia." MedlinePlus, 1 June 2025, medlineplus.gov/ency/article/007211. htm.

"Tick Removal: Medlineplus Medical Encyclopedia." MedlinePlus, medlineplus.gov/ency/article/007211.htm. Accessed 2023.

"Ticks and Lyme Disease." CDC.Gov, 27 Jan. 2020, www.cdc. gov/lyme/resources/toolkit/factsheets/10_508_Lyme%20 disease_PregnantWoman_FACTSheet.pdf.

"What Is Ozone Therapy?" Healthline, 12 Aug. 2020, www. healthline.com/health/ozone-therapy.

White, Tracie. "Potential Treatment for Lingering Lyme Disease." Stanford Medicine News Center, 12 Mar. 2020, med.stanford.edu/news/all-news/2020/03/potential-treatment-for-lingering-lyme-disease.html.